D1474353

1001
KNIGHTS

VOL I   COURAGE

With Foreword by Samantha Swords

DISCARDED
BY
BERTHOUD COMMUNITY
LIBRARY DISTRICT

THE GREAT WINDMILL

1001 Knights: Volume I: Courage is a work of fiction. Names, characters, businesses, places, events, incidents, dragons, castles, & swords are either the products of the author's imagination or used in a fictitious manner. Any resemblance to actual persons, dragons, or knights, living or dead, or actual events is purely coincidental.

1001 Knights Curated by Annie Stoll & Kevin Jay Stanton
Art Direction & Design by Annie Stoll
Cover Illustration & Crest by Kevin Jay Stanton

1001 Knights is a 3 volume people-positive anthology.
There are over 260 artists who participated in *1001 Knights*.
The book in your hands is Vol. I, Courage.

1001 Knights: Volume I: Courage Copyright © 2017 by The Great Windmill / 1001 Knights
All art within this book Copyright © 2017 their respective artists.

All rights reserved. This book or any portion thereof may not be reproduced or used in any manner whatsoever without the express written permission of the publisher except for the use of brief quotations in a book review or for educational purposes in classrooms and libraries. All rights for individual art, stories, and media within this anthology belong to their creators. No part of this book may be reproduced or transmitted in any form or by any means, electronic or mechanical, including photography, xerography, and video recording, without the express written permission from the publisher, The Great Windmill.

1001 Knights was made possible by our generous Kickstarter backers.
Please visit our website to view a full list of ther names at
www.OneThousandAndOneKnights.com/thankyou

Thank you to all the amazing artists. We hope that you, dear reader, check each of them out in the index & discover new and amazing worlds of art. Special thank you to the team who helped us created 1001 Knights: George Rohac & the Breadpig team, T.H., Shariq Ansari, Matt Pichette, Lillian Skye, & all our friends and family for believing in all of us and helping us make this project a reality.

Typefaces:
DropCaps are Ivory by Facetype Foundry. Ivory is inspired by a beautiful typeface used in an illustrated compendium about pomology from 1882. Body copy is Begum by Indian Type Foundry. The complete Begum super family was designed in India by Manushi Parikh. Logotype is based on Charcuterie Block a typeface created by Laura Worthington. Charcuterie is an homage to the inventiveness, passion, and care of peasants who proudly handed down recipes through generations.

First Printing, 2017

ISBN 978-0-9988204-0-8

www.OneThousandAndOneKnights.com | OneThousandAndOneKnights@gmail.com

"If one is lucky, a solitary fantasy
can totally transform a million realities."

—MAYA ANGELOU

1001 KNIGHTS is a people-positive project that started out as a small zine and grew into so much more. Years in the making, there are more than 260 artists and over 3,000 Kickstarter backers who made this book possible. When 1001 Knights was first conceived, we vowed that all artists were welcome regardless of gender, sexual identity, race, creed, or nationality.

The only question posed was "What does it mean to be a knight?" And we will let you, dear reader, enjoy and be inspired by the incredible imagination of the artists of 1001 Knights...

TABLE OF CONTENTS

FOREWORD

Courage is a core characteristic of a hero. Yet courage cannot exist without fear. If there is no fear to overcome, the hero never truly grows, finds new paths, overcomes great odds and does important deeds that benefit many.

Having fear is a vital part of being alive. It tells us where we shouldn't go, begs us to avoid risks and to stick to what is known. I have wrestled with fear almost my entire life and much of that has not been on the winning side.

Fear has been one of my most constant of companions since I was a child, whispering to me in every moment and gripping me forcefully when it is ignored. Fear is like a much smaller, very focused version of me- always alert and paranoid about danger.

When I don't pay attention to her warnings she gets anxious, and the more I push her away the more frantic and forceful she becomes in her child-like desperation for my attention. She creeps around the back of my mind, and then suddenly smothers me until I am blind and paralyzed by nameless terror; utterly confronted with all of the weakest parts of myself.

I can't disown or hate my fear. She means well, and she's good at keeping me alive. Instead, I have learned to listen to her early on, to dry her tears, take her hand and explain step by step how to safely deal with whatever awful thing she is so scared of.

There is no courage without fear.

For me, being 'courageous' or 'fearless' does not mean the absence of fear. They mean to be intimate with it, to really know the terror of something and then go ahead and do it anyway. Better still, to do so with joy, wild curiosity, and a celebration of life! 'What would happen if...?' can only be discovered when we leave the comfort of what is familiar and assured.

It's finding this space of being still, calm and in the moment - in the face of danger - that is hardest of all. For the knight this is pushing past pain and finding their flow amongst the violence of battle. For the artist, this is facing that blank canvas and being brave enough to give form to the ideas that come. It's in this fragile place of change and challange that the true magic happens, and where we can glimpse the greatest element of ourselves. This is what it is to be a hero.

A knight seeks to protect what they love, to stand and be strong for those who can't fight. The artist dreams to create something better than what already is, to show what is possible and lead the hearts of those open to imagination. The pen is the sword of the creative, and the battles fought in this invisible realm of ideas liberate great stories from the clutches of our own monsters.

Without fear to push against us, we'd never build the strength of will needed to do great and mighty things in the world. It takes courage to do what's right, to speak truth, to follow through and do what you say you are going to do. It takes guts to overcome our own failures. Every challenge is an opportunity to be strong.

Every person already has the power to do what is difficult. We can all dare to step forward and move against the forces of our mind that overwhelmingly tell us 'no'. Each tiny action builds up until one day we wake up and we're stronger than we ever knew we could be.

We can all be a hero - we just need to choose to be.

— SAMANTHA SWORDS

THE BLOODY QUEEN
BY BARBARA PEREZ-MARQUEZ

Her orders were ruthless. She wore a red scarf and a stern face.
Back when kingdoms attacked each other for power,
she lead her troops with an iron fist. Rumors said her armor had lost
its shine from the blood stains. They said her ruling would have no end.
An accepted tyranny.

The people knew there wasn't a more stable way to rule their land.
No mercy for the adversary, pity for the unfortunate ones left after the battle.
This system was at the core of the kingdom.

Their tall horses marched down the streets of their city;
back from another successful campaign, their queen at the front of the march.
No colorful parade, this was just another victory. Their people still cheered them
for their return, before going back to their everyday business.

The troops looked forward to the mundane, regaining their energies after
the battle and attending any small injuries. No casualties, they hardly lost any
men when they fought. Some said it was because they had a fated blessing,
some others said the queen commanded a cursed army. No one dared find out the truth.

After the march, the troops went to rest and celebrate.
The queen never celebrated with them, she simply retired to her castle to recover
and would only come out the day after, when the troops were regrouped for training.
As she walked deeper into the castle walls, the cheers of the troops starting to celebrate
disappeared and soon it was only her steps and her two maids'.

She pushed open a pair of doors and let out a breath as she stood in the center
of the grand bathroom. The two maids stepped forward and took off her armor and dress,
allowing the queen to slip into the bath waiting for her.

The two maids bowed and left the bathroom and the queen took her time in the warm water.
She thought about the campaign that had just passed and her kingdom, looking out the window
towards the setting sun. Let them have the rest of the day, tomorrow she would be back in her
throne. She busied herself scrubbing at her palms. Scrub away the impurities,
so her kingdom didn't have to.

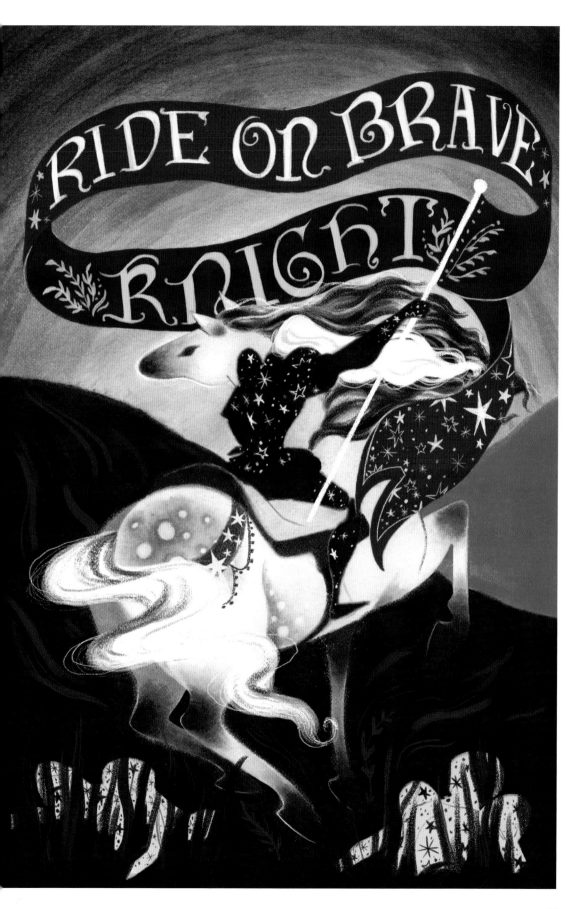

Sir Gawain and the Loathly Lady

Emily Cheeseman

One day, King Arthur of Camelot was hunting in the forest of Inglewood when a menacing figure in pitch black armor approached to challenge him.

CURSED KING! YOU HAVE DONE ME WRONG AND WOEFULLY I SHALL REPAY YOU NOW.

The king asked the terrible knight the cause of his anger, to which he replied,

KILLING YOU HERE WILL GIVE ME NO GLORY,

BUT I DEMAND SATISFACTION NONETHELESS.

SIR! the king exclaimed,

SPARE MY LIFE AND ASK ANYTHING — I WILL GRANT IT.

IF YOU WOULD WIN YOUR LIFE, RETURN HERE IN TWELVE DAYS' TIME WITH AN ANSWER TO THIS QUESTION —

WHAT DOES EVERY WOMAN DESIRE MOST?

And the knight was gone as quicky as he came.

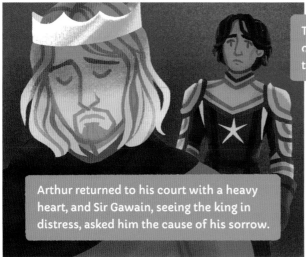

The king related the tale of his encounter with the Wicked Knight.

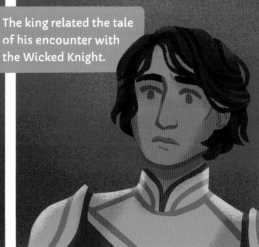

Arthur returned to his court with a heavy heart, and Sir Gawain, seeing the king in distress, asked him the cause of his sorrow.

Sir Gawain then proposed they ride forth and ask every woman they encountered what she most desired.

Soon they had a book filled with answers.

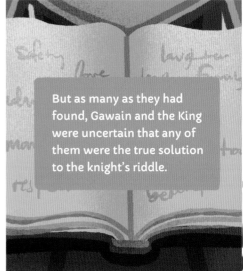

But as many as they had found, Gawain and the King were uncertain that any of them were the true solution to the knight's riddle.

As the end of the twelve days neared, Gawain came upon a clearing in a forest,

where a woman stood in his path.

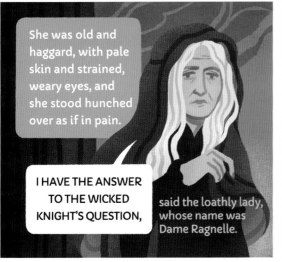

She was old and haggard, with pale skin and strained, weary eyes, and she stood hunched over as if in pain.

I HAVE THE ANSWER TO THE WICKED KNIGHT'S QUESTION, said the loathly lady, whose name was Dame Ragnelle.

I WILL GIVE IT TO YOU, IF YOU GRANT ME ONE REQUEST.

GOOD LADY, MY THANKS, FOR IF YOUR ANSWER IS THE ONE I SEEK, IT WILL SAVE THE KING'S LIFE.

WHAT IS YOUR PRICE?

THAT YOU BRING ME TO THE ROYAL COURT AT CARLISLE, AND TAKE ME FOR YOUR WIFE.

IT IS MY DUTY TO PROTECT THE KING. IF WHAT YOU GIVE ME IS THE TRUE SOLUTION TO THE KNIGHT'S RIDDLE,

THEN I WILL CONSENT.

THEN HERE IS YOUR ANSWER.

WHAT DOES EVERY WOMAN DESIRE MOST? THERE ARE AS MANY ANSWERS AS THERE ARE WOMEN IN THE WORLD. ADMIRATION, LAUGHTER, STRENGTH, SAFETY - EVEN LOVE AND BEAUTY.

BUT MOST OF ALL, AND SIMPLEST OF ALL — WHAT WOMEN DESIRE MOST, SIR KNIGHT, IS SOVEREIGNTY OVER THEMSELVES. THE FREEDOM TO MAKE THEIR OWN DECISIONS.

At the end of twelve days, Arthur met once more with the Black Knight, who roared in frustration upon hearing the king's response.

ONLY THAT CURSED HAG COULD HAVE GIVEN YOU THIS ANSWER! MAY SHE SUFFER FOR HER TREACHERY!

And the Wicked Knight was gone for good.

Sir Gawain and the Lady Ragnelle were married at court the next day.

The guests were appalled to see such a handsome knight married to such a hideous woman.

But Gawain felt only pity for the lady who was met with such scorn on her wedding day.

The feast ended at sundown, and the couple retired to the knight's chamber.

KIND HUSBAND,

the lady said,

WILL YOU NOT LOOK UPON YOUR WIFE?

Gawain was stunned to find the loveliest woman standing before him.

She was hale and fair, and her eyes were bright— The Loathly Lady was no more.

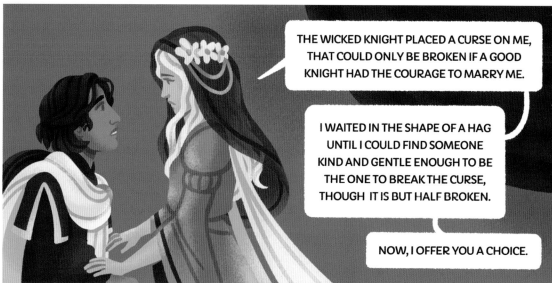

THE WICKED KNIGHT PLACED A CURSE ON ME, THAT COULD ONLY BE BROKEN IF A GOOD KNIGHT HAD THE COURAGE TO MARRY ME.

I WAITED IN THE SHAPE OF A HAG UNTIL I COULD FIND SOMEONE KIND AND GENTLE ENOUGH TO BE THE ONE TO BREAK THE CURSE, THOUGH IT IS BUT HALF BROKEN.

NOW, I OFFER YOU A CHOICE.

I CAN BE FOUL BY NIGHT AND FAIR BY DAY, WHEN ALL OTHERS CAN SEE ME

OR I CAN BE FOUL BY DAY AND FAIR BY NIGHT, WHEN ONLY YOU CAN SEE ME.

DECIDE WHICH YOU WANT.

the cloud fades

and I descend

upon the

enemy

I am known by many names.
Angel of Death. Demon of Life.
Keeper of spells. Knight of Day.
The Girl in the Cat or Bear Jacket.

Violence cannot harm me.
Yet peace remains elusive.

Alex Chautin

There were hunters and gatherers, providers and creators. But that was a short-lived fantasy. Such a luxury no longer exists in the clay. What are we searching for in the long-expended crust of the underneath? What can we collect to feed our children, our sick, and our selfishly aching hunger?

Must be that I'll know if I ever find it. I keep digging.

As much time as I spend out here, as tanned as my hide gets, the back of my neck is still a canvas stretched by the unforgiving hand of the heavens.

To be a collector, you've gotta dig deep. Use the desperation of that first drink of warm newly-cleaned water after the two-week wait for the   unpredictable rainfaill lucky enough to be collected   or sink generously into our domain.

My guardians labor away at their community job as water pump operators, and as usual a 10-hour day accumulates less than a gallon of water per operator, still filled with churned sediment.

Particles sink to the bottom of a clear glass as if they too had given up and retreated downward for fear of being consumed by the thirsty, entitled surface-dwelers who hoard their oasis   without a thought of our difficulty.

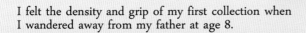

I felt the density and grip of my first collection when I wandered away from my father at age 8.

I sat there under the parasol. Too hot to understand that what sat next to me was all the water we would recieve for the next few days, I wandered into the scorching world.

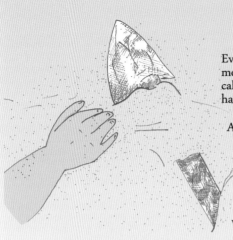

Even my darkened skin was hardly enough to keep me conscious when I went too far to hear my father call my name, once he looked up from his day's harvest.

A blunt pain haunted my toes and my knee kissed the ground, a fierce light blinded my cave-adjusted, foolishly uncovered eyes, and I did not see the dunes' decline only inches from my feet.

I recognized the texture under my hand when I awoke.

It was burning material - hard to come by cheaply but we used it to keep warm in the cold seasons by rubbing it with stone. Stone was and is certainly plentiful. But there was more. Attached to it was something even more precious, a shape I did not recognize. It resembled a pair of hands, cupped to recieve water or an offering of food. Though instead of fingers there was a sharp border that outlined it, leading to an intimidating point.

When I returned to my father, who in a fit of anguish at the thought of my disappearance now held a half-spilled container of sandy water, I proudly and unknowingly presented my prize.

As more tears welled from his cheeks, he cried that this tool would help us find a new better water well.

And it did. I haven't gone thirsty since.

Furthermore, my collection has continued to grow and emerge from beneath my feet. This tool grants me a different sort of harvest. Who knows...

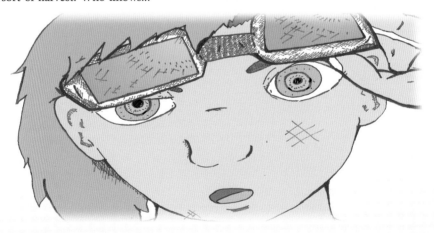

The sun and the stars have slowly meandered on their way, silently, violently, and uncaring of us. And I search further...we all search further,

Perhaps that light will shine down again so that we may find another treasure, a lost relic, to recapture the oasis and to our relief, survive even a little bit better.

To fight just a little longer.

45

SPIRITS

BY ALEX CHIU

TAIPEI, TAIWAN

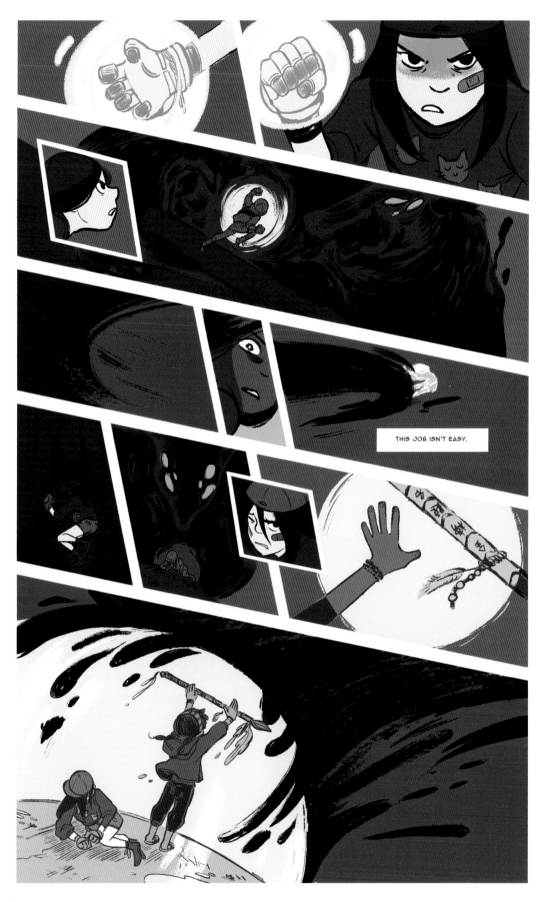

THIS JOB ISN'T EASY.

SORRY I'M LATE! FORGOT IT WAS MY TURN TO GET SNACKS FOR TONIGHT!

BUT THANKFULLY, YOU'RE NEVER ALONE.

DID IT REALLY TAKE YOU THAT LONG FOR A BOX OF POCKY?

OF COURSE NOT! I GOT 3 BOXES OF STRAWBERRY POCKY, AND GREEN TEA, TOO.

AH! MY FAVORITES! YOU'RE THE BEST!

HEH! I REMEMBER THAT DAY WHEN YOU HOARDED LIKE TEN THINGS OF GREEN TEA.

AHAHAHA! YOU KNOW ME TOO WELL. I'M GLAD THAT'S THE LASTING IMAGE YOU'LL HAVE OF ME, HAH.

WELL, YOU WITH TEN BOTTLES OF GREEN TEA AND ME WITH FIFTY BOXES OF ALL SORTS OF POCKY...

OH MY GOD. WATCH OUT SPIRIT DEMONS, HERE WE COME, WITH SNACKS AND FRIENDSHIP.

[LAUGHS] OK, OK, NEXT TIME WE'RE DEFINITELY DOING THAT.

END

ARE YOU SURE YOU DON'T HAVE ANY OPENINGS FOR KNIGHTS? OR EVEN A SQUIRE?

THIS IS AN INN. THE KNIGHT'S ONLY OUR LOGO.

YA GOTTA HELP ME! I WANNA BE AN AWESOME LADY KNIGHT! YOU KNOW, LIKE YOU READ ABOUT IN THE PAPERS! SLAYING DRAGONS AND HEARTS IN THE RICHEOUS PURSUIT OF JUSTICE!

JUST BECAUSE WE'RE NOT HIRING KNIGHTS HERE DOESN'T MEAN YOU CAN'T PURSUE YOUR DREAMS.

BUT I WANNA SLAY STUFF....

THERE'S MORE TO BEING A KNIGHT THAN DEMONS AND DAMSELS...

UM..

WHAT WAS THAT? I CAN'T HEAR YOU OVER THE SOUND OF HOW AWESOME A KNIGHT I'M GONNA BE!

IS THAT FROM MY WALL

Blossom

Lion

By

Rachel L. Cohen

My name is Smadar.

It means 'blossom' in an ancient tongue.

I was once a monster, created by an evil Skeleton Witch.

But I was rescued by the Princess of this faraway land.

Now she is Queen,

and I am her Champion.

When the Skeleton Witch returned
to devour my Queen,

I had to become a monster once more,

and I slew them.

Never again shall darkness try to devour my Queen,

for she has her monster to protect her.

Her Blossom Lion.

TO EVE, WHEN THERE ARE SNAKES AND NO LADDERS
BY CARIS CRUZ

It's official: they have placed
"World's Greatest Offender" right before
your name. Your folly has led to the declension of man.
The first of many.

But I digress, we all have snakes
slithering inside our stomachs, telling lies,
bribing apples. You took one but
others took many; some even more than fruit.

Dearest, don't hide behind a bush,
you have been naked long before you knew it.
Being bare, howbeit, is different from being stripped
of your conscience.

Your soul is beautifully lodged
within your intestines.
You never lost it.

Don't shudder when they mention your name
with reproach. Sin wasn't
originally in your DNA.
But everyone takes a big fall from grace.

Tell humankind you are brave.
Climb from that slope with your own two feet.

Scream at them with your birth pains, that your
umbilical cords became a passageway
of life, of breath,
of heartbeats, of voices.

Man will label you but he can
never break you. He's made of dirt.
Of mud. Of clay.
But you are made of ribs, of bones.

You are strong. You are relentless.

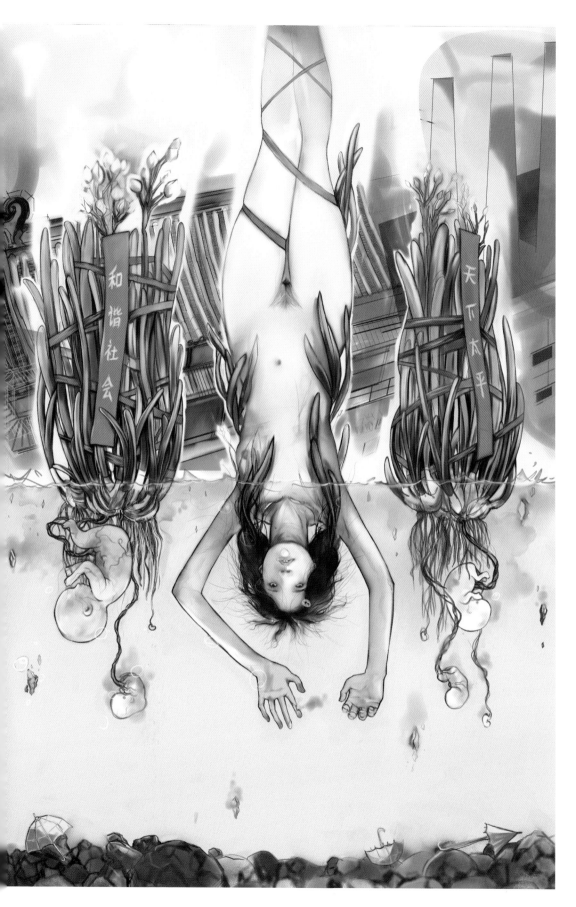

ESPADA
KNIGHTS

ESPADA
KNIGHTS

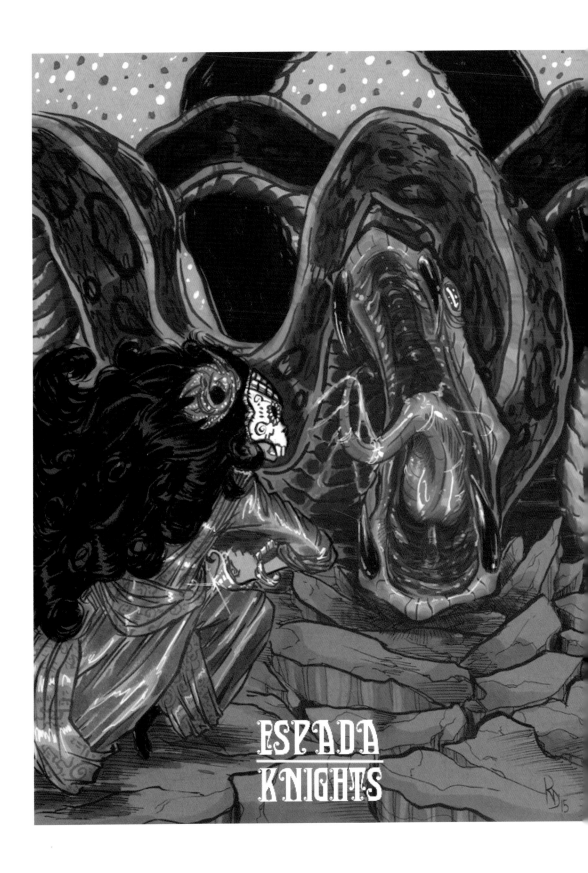

ESPADA
KNIGHTS

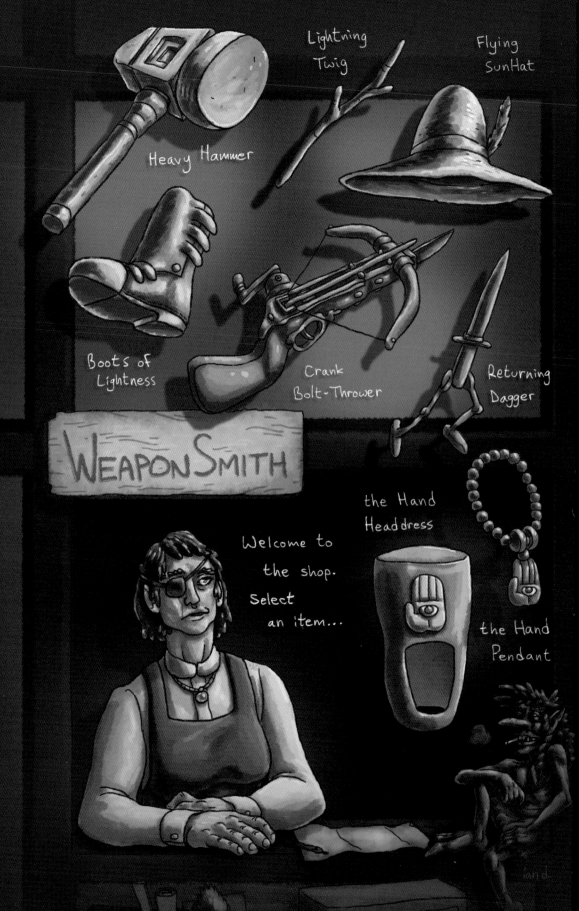

THE SNOW GIANT
BY MATTHEW K HODDY

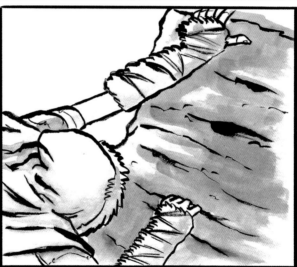

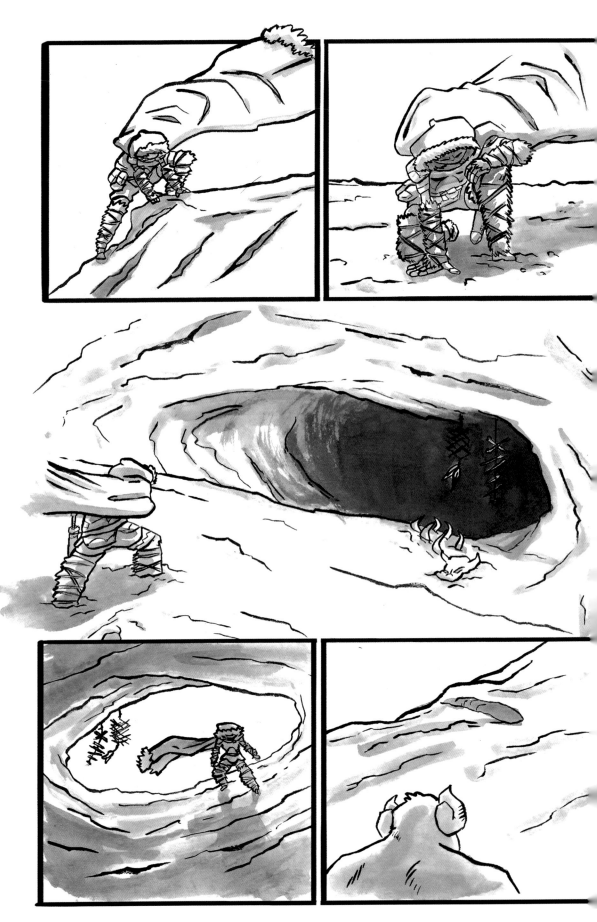

HRNN

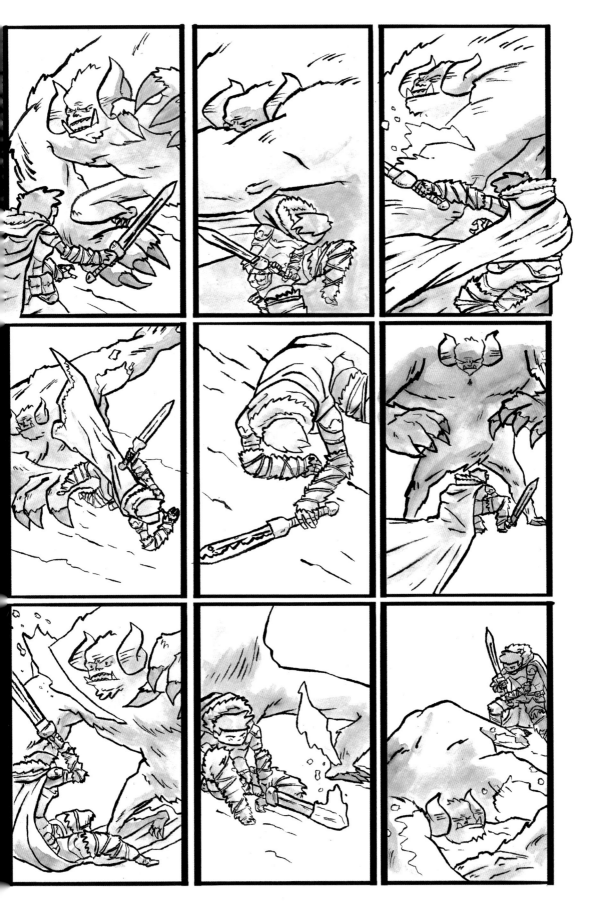

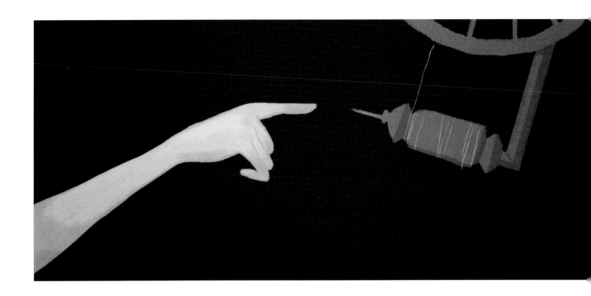

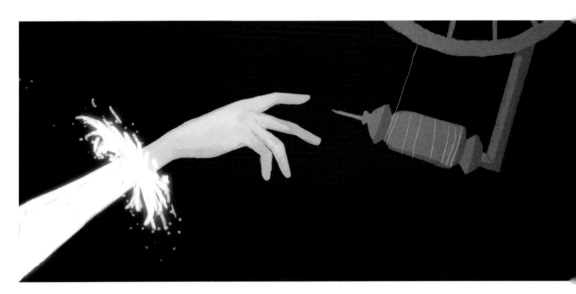

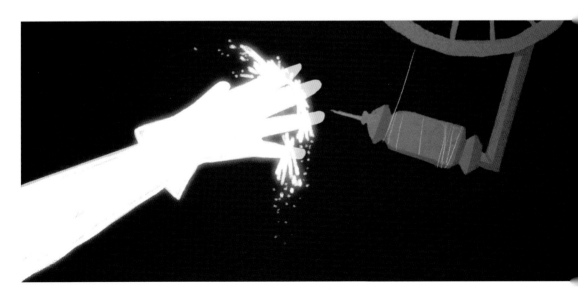

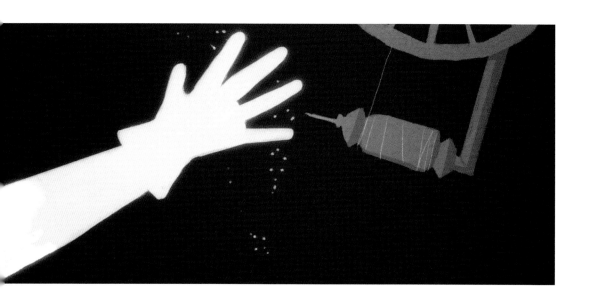

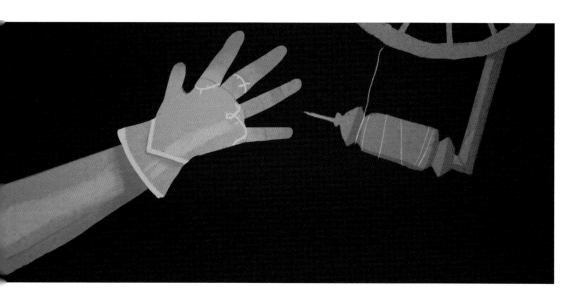

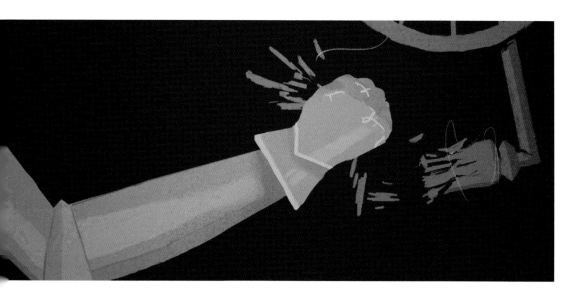

The air is abloom.

The horizon flutters with ominous petals.

END
107

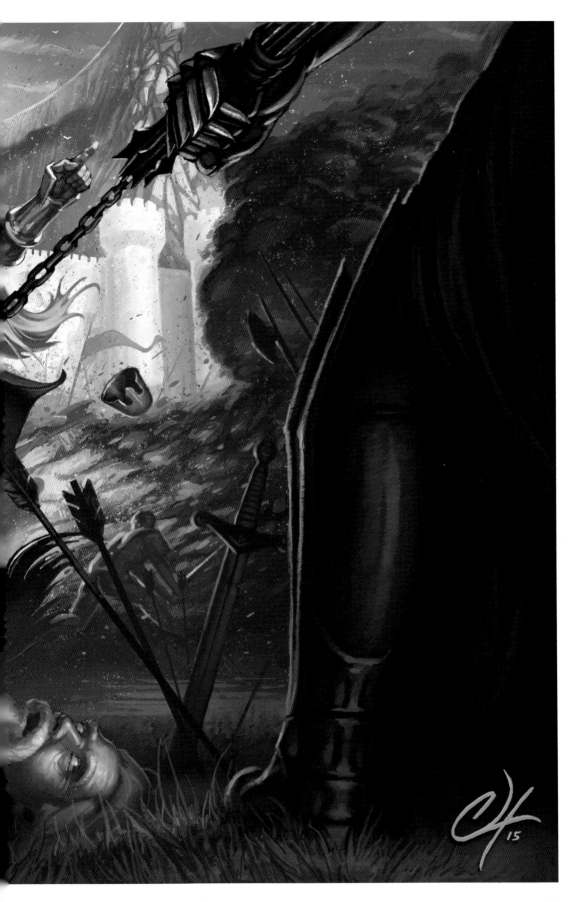

PRINCESS/KNIGHT

STORY & ART - KATA KANE

Let's keep moving forward...

Will you scout ahead for us?

NOD

LIFT

My life was given as a princess.

I was set on the path of fate
the moment I arrived in this world.

Countless expectations placed upon me
before I could even focus on the light...

...or recognize
the dark.

Are these not the qualities

we should also expect of a knight?

The
other
life,
we
make.

I'll earn this life
with devotion.

All I have,
I'll **give**.

As a
Princess.

As a
Knight.

/END

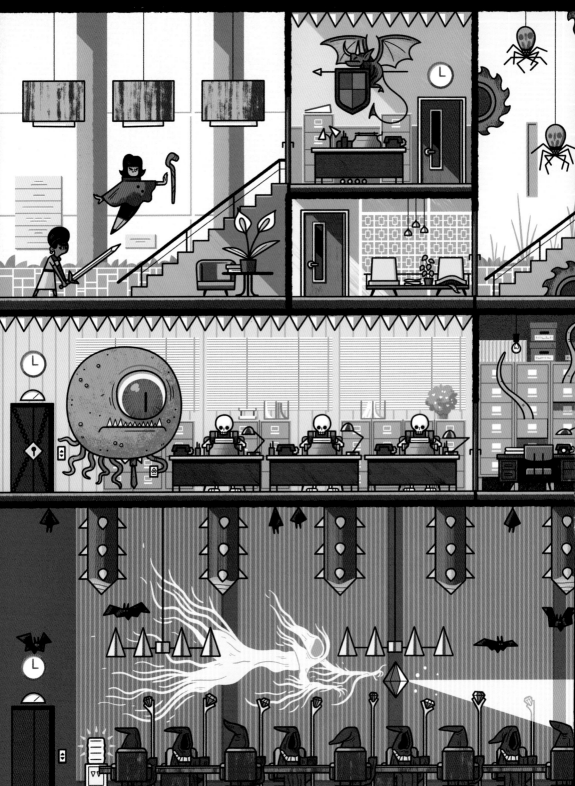

ARMOR
BY BARBARA PEREZ-MARQUEZ

You do not require
a quest to wear protection;
no dragon to defeat.
A weapon of choice is good
outside of the battlefield too.

Some days we need to protect
things that can't wear pauldrons,
carry shields to defend us from air.

Other days we must remove
every defense spell,
in order to breathe.

The GROVE KNIGHT

MANY YEARS AGO, A YOUNG GIRL DISAPPEARED IN TO THE WOODS, NEVER TO BE SEEN AGAIN.

SOME LEGENDS SAY THE GIRL WANDERED OFF ONLY TO BE EATEN BY WILD BEASTS, OTHERS THAT SHE BECOME A WANDERING SPIRIT.

BUT MANY BELIEVE THE GIRL WAS TAKEN BY A WITCH, DEEP INTO THE WOODS...

...AND WAS LOCKED AWAY IN A TOWER IN A HIDDEN GROVE.

THE PRISONER
BY DEVIN MCKERNAN

At the edge of the mountain road, a young squire of sixteen years caressed her brown mare's mane. An azure cloak, too large for the lanky frame underneath, caught the wind and billowed like a sail behind her. Lips set in a solemn line beneath a pair of anxious green eyes, the girl stared over the cliff at the forest rustling in the valley below.

"I could swear I saw something," the young woman mumbled to herself as she tightened her grip on the sword at her waist. She thrust a finger toward the creaking, verdant depths. Two black shadows darted back and forth amid the overgrowth. "There! Right there among those trees!"

The woodland's canopy, submerged beneath a shroud of darkening mist, stretched from the base of the mountain to the horizon like a bed of leaves for the stone giants looming above. A solitary, dismal howl echoed upward. Ears stiff and eyes wide, the girl's horse tilted her head, whinnied, and stomped back from the threshold. Cooing, the squire put a tender hand to the beast's neck.

"Steady the horses! The storm's nearly upon us!" A woman bellowed from behind, voice full of youthful bravado.

Mounted high upon a restless steed and wielding a great silver spear, a knight clad in plate armor shouted to the company of soldiers at her back. Etched on her chest was the sigil of dawn, engraved lines of light spreading from the symbol's center and glinting in the sunset. The knight's black hair danced on the wind as she swung a leg over her dapple grey and dropped to the mountain path with a thud. Within seconds a blanket of heavy clouds smothered the last light of day and bathed the crags in gloom.

Her face a mask of stoic resolve, the knight yanked a golden cloak over her armor and raised a gauntlet. At the sign, nine men and women dismounted their horses in unison, faces grim, armor clattering. As each wrapped their leather reins tight around their wrists, the knight's guards struck sparks to oil and set torches ablaze. The glowering faces beneath the dusty gray cloaks eyed one another in silent apprehension.

"Aveline!" The knight shouted to the girl. At the sound of her name, the youth was startled from her thoughts and hurried toward her commander. "Aveline, we haven't time to dally."

"Sir Julia, I…" Aveline started, but the knight's admonishing gaze demanded silence. The girl's brown mare snorted anxiously as she trotted in place. Looking at the wide-eyed creature, Aveline tried again. "Sir Julia, I think a pair of wolves has our scent."

"We've spent weeks hunting a beast. Wolves are the least of my concerns," Julia chuckled, waving her glimmering hand in dismissal. Thunder rumbled on the mountainside, as though the giants were alive and snoring. The knight narrowed her brown eyes at the sky above, then returned them to Aveline. "Attend the prisoner, squire. See she doesn't drown."

"Yes, Sir Julia," the girl said, her face red as coals beneath days of dust and grime. A handful of snickering smiles spread wide beneath the soldiers' burning torches. Aveline shot a sidelong glance at the jeering guards, but eager to hide her crimson cheeks, she turned from the knight and pulled her cloak up over a mess of hazel hair.

Slowly, the squire approached the ill-fated cargo lashed to her horse. A woman's form, bound and bent, lay silent across the beast's back. Wrapped in a dingy shawl, her shrouded head and roped feet dangled like saddlebags on the creature's flanks. As Aveline reached out a hand to touch the prisoner, lightning spread bright fingers above the dark mountains and with a roar set the sky to weeping. A chorus of snorts and whinnies burst from the startled horses as the soldiers clamored to regain control.

Over the discord, Aveline thought she heard the prisoner laugh.

Rain fell with the weight of stone and in moments each traveler was soaked and bruised. Flickering flames hissed and trembling steeds huffed. Still, the proud knight would not be deterred. As if to challenge the booming voice of the clouds above, she cupped a hand to her mouth and shouted over the riotous torrent.

"Tempest be damned – we push on to the city!" Julia cried. And though her words were drowned amid peals of crackling thunder, the soldiers offered a loyal cheer in return. Aveline frowned in dismay.

Reins in one hand and spear in the other, the knight pointed down the dark path and marched ahead. One by one, the others followed in single file, heads bowed to avoid the rain and watch the contours of the cliff. Parched dirt drank deep of the relentless shower and within minutes the road was drenched and slick.

For a time it seemed the storm would be only an unruly nuisance. But alas, fortune and fate are fickle masters.

Without warning, a chunk of the mountain gave way to the pitiless deluge. Aveline's horse saw its doom first, ears perked at the rumbling that was not thunder. In a second the beast was wild with fear, bucking and thrashing the girl holding her reins. As the boulders crashed into the mountain road, the night exploded in deafening calamity. Soldiers and steeds dodged and scattered. Mud and stone trampled forth. The girl's mare dashed for illusive safety, dragging Aveline toward death.

Before any could intervene, squire, horse, and prisoner plunged screaming over the edge into the darkness below.

* * *

Body awash in pain and mud, Aveline awoke to the sounds of scraping tree limbs, battered leaves, and vicious bickering. Beneath a sputtering torch, the knight and the prisoner exchanged a flurry of tense words despite the torrent around them.

"You thought it best to dive after us, nothing but a torch and spear at hand?" The prisoner scolded, raising bound wrists to point in accusation. "That the kind of nonsense they're teaching knights these days?"

Aveline flinched at the words' familiar tone. The prisoner's shroud had been discarded in the mud, revealing an ancient face etched by time. Deep lines traced the woman's eyes and cheeks, pale remnants of old scars scattered throughout. A cascade of drenched hair, black as night despite her age and not unlike Julia's, fell over her serious brow and broad shoulders. Though the prisoner was little more than a bent shadow amid the darkness, her posture was that of a captive animal: head still and limbs ready, waiting to escape her bonds.

"You don't find it cruel, them sending a daughter to hunt her mother?" The prisoner chided.

"Not when her mother's a traitor," Julia retaliated. "You tried to kill our king!"

"The monster killed your father!" Roared the prisoner.

Aveline's breath caught in her throat. At the sound, the knight hefted her silver spear and glared toward the girl as if ready to attack. Surprised to see her squire awake, Julia trotted through the mud to Aveline's side and held out a silver hand. The girl shook her aching head, bewildered by the conversation. She knew they hunted a treasonous assassin, but that betrayer was Sir Julia's mother? The prisoner's furious accusation sent a cold tremor through Aveline's body. The girl pushed her tangled wet hair out of her eyes and grabbed the knight's outstretched gauntlet.

"I'm sorry to have caused so much trouble," Aveline murmured as she climbed to her feet.

"Don't blame yourself. It's her fault we're out here," Julia said. The girl's heart beat fast in her chest.

"And I suppose it was my idea to forego the village ten miles back and push on through this nasty business? Forgive me, my old mind isn't what it once was... I seem to have forgotten I had command of the company," the old woman scowled, before raising her open mouth to the sky for a drink. A blast of thunder boomed overhead.

"Forgive my mother. She once knew respect, but hasn't kept polite company for some time," the knight said.

"'Polite company.' Ha. You abduct an old woman, then question my manners?" The prisoner growled. "What happened to you?"

"You happened to me," Julia spat.

Aveline shook her head in amazement, then stared intently at the knight and the prisoner. The resemblance between the two was uncanny. When the knight opened her mouth to speak again, a weary voice cut through the din of the rustling forest around the three women.

"Sir Julia!" A man cried from above. "Sir Julia, are you all right? Is the prisoner alive?"

"We're fine! Press on to the city! We'll rally at dawn!" Julia shouted, waving her torch. Raindrops ringing like chimes on her armor, the knight turned to her companions. "Gather what you can and we'll set out. To linger in the dark would be folly."

The prisoner rolled her eyes. Aveline approached the lifeless form of her fallen steed on weak, shaking legs. Surveying the mangled horse, Aveline could barely believe she or the old woman had survived their fall. The girl knelt by the mare's side and reached out to caress her scattered, chestnut mane.

"Thank you, friend. Forgive me," Aveline whispered beneath the noise of the rainfall. With one last touch to the creature's fragile neck, the squire rose and salvaged what she could. In minutes, Aveline recovered a short sword, a shield, and a pack filled with rations and rudimentary medical supplies. The squire looked to the knight's torch. "I have a book of flash paper for light, if this storm ever relents."

"Let's pray to Dawn it does," Julia murmured.

The knight and the prisoner trudged away from the cliff, but Aveline paused in her steps.

Icy fingers of warning creeped up the girl's spine, as though unseen eyes were upon her. Beneath the cacophony of the storm, Aveline would have sworn she heard a menacing, feral growl. A memory of black shadows flashed in her mind as the girl peered into the forest through the torch's mercurial light. It seemed nothing looked back from the darkness, but still the girl trembled, clutching the straps of the soaked canvas satchel on her back. Aveline looked once more at the lifeless horse, exhaled a shallow breath, and turned to catch her companions.

The three marched on, mighty trees looming beside their path like abyssal sentinels cloaked in charcoal shrouds. An hour passed beneath the rain's persistent drums. As quickly as it had arrived, the thunderstorm abandoned its torrential siege, sparing the unfortunate souls below from a night of further torment. The wayfarers welcomed the reprieve, but three hours since the cliff,

Julia's frustration was plain.

"We should have been there by now," Julia mumbled to herself, holding her torch aloft. The fire atop the wooden baton flickered and wavered on the verge of death.

"You know, of course, that we've been traveling the wrong direction for some time," the old woman remarked. She turned her ancient face on Aveline and smiled. "But maybe you'd like to enlighten her?"

"Me, I..." Aveline stammered.

"I've seen you looking skyward. Which way's home, girl?" The prisoner's eyes were two pools of ink.

"Well, that's – that's the Stag's Eye," Aveline murmured. She peered up to the purple sky and pointed at the brightest of the shining dots. "If we turn left and continue north, we should make the city by morning."

"Oh, I like this girl. Reminds me of someone I once knew," the prisoner chortled. Julia sighed in exasperation and stopped. "Don't worry, I wasn't talking about you, sir. Who was your mother?"

"That's quite enough," the knight snapped. The old woman glowered at her daughter, eyes ablaze. Glancing between mother and daughter, Aveline raised a hand for peace.

"My name is Aveline, of House Drummond," the girl whispered. "Daughter to Rayner and Hannah."

"Those eyes, that hair, that blue cloak. You do so take after your mother," the prisoner said. Aveline blushed and stared at the dirt passing by beneath her boots. "My name is Margot, of House... Well, that doesn't matter. Tell me, Aveline, what's become of my old friends?"

Aveline grew quiet, but the knight spoke up in her stead.

"They're dead, mother. Murdered in their home before her," Julia hissed, her voice full of contempt.

Before Margot could respond, the three travelers were stunned to silence. A monstrous roar shook the forest like an echo of the twilight storm. From the orange gloom at the edge of the torch's dying light, a pair of enormous wolves stepped forward, their faces and limbs encased in shards of black crystal. Long, obsidian claws dug deep into the wet dirt as strings of shimmering saliva fell from ravenous jaws. Four empty eyes glared at the humans.

"Stay behind me!" Julia shouted, lowering her spear and raising her torch.

"Set me free," the prisoner growled. "I can still fight."

"Why should I trust you?" Julia snapped.

A guttural howl burst from the wolves' cavernous, jagged maws on a gust of carrion breath. Glancing at the creatures and then at her mother, the knight sighed. From her belt she grabbed a knife and cleaved the ropes wrapped around the prisoner's wrists. Flipping the knife, Julia offered its hilt and thrust the torch forward, its flame nearly spent. Margot grabbed both and smirked.

Aveline pushed her mouth to her blue cloak, breathed deep for comfort, then drew her sword and mounted her shield on her arm. The girl stepped behind Julia, shield raised high to cover the knight's flank. Wary green eyes shifted back and forth beneath a sweat-drenched brow.

As the corrupted creatures stalked and snarled, the knight flung her gold cloak back over her moonlit shoulders and traced a wide arc with her silver lance. The single-minded beasts sprinted toward the travelers, their heavy, thunderous steps shaking the earth beneath each stride. Branches snapped, mud splattered, and in a moment the slavering wolves were upon their prey.

The knight charged the creatures, armor glittering in the starlight. As the wolves attacked, Julia battered one with the shaft of her weapon and thrust its blade at the jaws of the other. The shining edge bit deep into the demon's gloom-ridden face, shattering flesh amid a cloud of exploding shadow. Howling in pain, the animal leapt away.

The knight smiled wide, but within seconds the beast's companion was dashing forward. Aveline lifted her shield. As she set her boots in the muck, the wolf crashed into the broad metal wall. Jets of hot breath barraged Aveline's face as she pushed against the crystalline creature's weight and hacked at it with her sword. In a moment, Margot was beside her, adding her strength to the struggle. Claws raked the shield's groaning edges.

"Push!" The prisoner howled to the girl, but their effort could not dissuade the beast.

Screaming at her quarry, Julia sprang forward and plunged her lance into the grizzled fur on the great wolf's flank. An otherworldly shriek erupted from the beast's snapping jaws. The smell of copper filled the air as blood gushed to the ground. Aveline marveled at the knight's ferocity. The thrashing beast snarled and bounded toward Julia, who stepped casually out of the creature's path as it sprinted back into the forest.

The knight grinned in victory. The squire gaped in horror.

Before Aveline's cry of warning could reach Julia's ears, the shattered jaws of her first opponent snapped shut on her shining arm. The wolf swung its sharp head and the knight was flung to the dirt. Her gauntlet crushed and drenched with blood, Julia stood on tremulous legs, then collapsed to her knees. The world was silent and gray as Aveline sprinted toward the knight, Margot but a step behind. It was then that warm glow of the torch's light was extinguished, submerging the scene in darkness.

The stubborn beast's black form glided like a wraith amid the gloom. Fallen leaves and pools of rain crumpled and splashed beneath the onyx claws just out of sight. Aveline squinted into the forest, frantically tracking the phantom's movements with her shield.

"Flash paper! Now!" Margot commanded the squire.

Aveline thrust her sword in the dirt, then unslung her pack and let it fall behind her. The old woman set upon it, ripping open its buckles and scouring its contents. In a moment, the prisoner held a small booklet, then tore out a handful of its pages. On each was traced a strange sigil, interlocking lines and geometry set in an arcane sign of flame and light.

"Forgive me," Margot muttered. Julia moaned and reached toward her mother.

Without another word, the prisoner raised her knife and brought its hilt down on the back of her daughter's head. Eyes blank, face lifeless, Julia plummeted again with a crash of armor to the mud. Aveline gasped in shock as Margot glared at the circling creature and screamed in challenge. Amid a blinding flash and burst of smoke, the prisoner stabbed a handful of paper onto her blade and waved it to gain the wolf's attention.

Margot cast a dark, knowing eye at Aveline, then vanished among the shadows, the crystalline beast in pursuit.

* * *

The first shafts of dawn's light were piercing the forest canopy when Julia's eyes finally opened. At the sight of fluttering eyelids, Aveline yelped in surprise and elation. After two frantic hours spent stripping the knight's tarnished plate and mending countless wounds, the girl's hands were stained and shaking. A wet spool of black string and crimson needle rested upon a broad leaf by her side.

"What happened? Where has she gone?" Julia groaned as she put a palm to her blood-caked forehead.

"She fled in the night," Aveline said. "I think she meant to draw that monster away,"

"Or to escape me," Julia murmured. Shaking her head, Aveline pointed north.

"She left a trail," the girl explained as she crouched and dipped her hands in a pool of rainwater.

Some paces off, an uneven line of smoldering paper led away from the churned mud and dirt of the battleground. Despite the tiny rivers running wild on the forest floor, the paper still burned bright and loud. Wisps of smoke drifted on a gentle breeze up toward the chattering tree tops.
"You lost a lot of blood," the girl frowned. "Perhaps we should wait to recover? What about your armor?"

"Leave it. I can't let her get away," Julia growled. "My life may depend on it."

The knight grabbed hold of the spear resting in the dirt beside her and braced herself. Stumbling to her feet, Julia thrust out a hand, which Aveline caught before her commander could fall. With a glance at the pile of gouged plate, Aveline stepped beneath Julia's shoulder as a crutch. Step by halting step, the squire led her knight past the trees and bright scraps of errant paper. The carcass of a freshly slain wolf lay across their path, a dozen skillful wounds in its bloodied flesh and fur. The knight's silver knife sat buried to its hilt in the creature's lifeless neck.

As they walked, Julia eyed the damp, muddy fabric clinging to Aveline's shoulders.

"I've heard rumors of your mother's cloak; that she weaved magic into its blue threads," the knight said.

The squire voiced no reply as she guided her charge across a fresh, rain-carved trench. Her boots slipping on wet leaves, the knight winced when she struggled to regain her grip on the spear.

"You must be proud to call her kin," Julia muttered between clenched teeth.

"I'd rather she were alive," Aveline said. The younger woman's voice was hushed, but cool with ire, as she stared into the somber, storm-ravaged forest ahead.

It was an hour before the ragged pair emerged from the edge of the woodland. A low, crumbling stone wall stretched down into a bayside valley, encircling the abundant expanse of farmland that surrounded the great castle city looming in the distance. The clear morning light that followed in the storm's wake drenched the parapets, towers, and water beyond in rich tones of amber and gold. Head crowned and sword held aloft, a colossal stone man presided over the buildings and streets that had expanded through centuries beneath him.

"Home," Aveline whispered, looking wide-eyed at the king around which the city crowded and turned. Indifferent, Julia nudged her squire to press on.

After a dozen paces, the girl cried out, rushed from beneath the knight's arm, and then froze. Sprawled out on her back amid a circle of burning paper, Margot stared up at a cloudless blue sky through half-closed eyes. Aveline gulped and thrust a hand to her mouth, fearing the old woman was dead.

At the sight of her mother, Julia staggered forth, silver spear quavering by her side. Silent and solemn, the knight loomed over the prisoner, her face a blank silhouette. Margot appeared ashen and haggard, her black cloak shredded to red-stained tatters. Aveline clenched her fists and looked away, afraid to utter a word.

"Was wondering when you'd catch up," the old woman winced as she struggled to lean back on her elbows. Despite the blood-painted grass beneath her, Margot's lips were parted in a toothy grin as pale as her skin. "Been so long since last I saw this dreadful place. The walls, that towering monstrosity. It really is hideous. Ruins the horizon. But I suppose this is it then. Time to deliver my old bones to justice?"

"I should kill you now and save the king the trouble of your judgment," Julia snarled, tear-filled eyes flashing with frustration and fury.

The knight brought her weapon to bear on the old woman, who for her part only smiled. Before she could think, Aveline sprang forward to stand between the knight and her mother, arms spread wide in protest. The blue cloak draped around her shoulders snapped on a blast of cool wind. The small heart within her heaving chest thundered loud.

"This isn't right!" Aveline shouted, voice firm, eyes forbidding. "Your mother saved our lives."

Julia stared at her squire, fury snuffed out by bewilderment. The blade of her spear quivered inches from the girl's breast, but the stony grimace upon Aveline's face was unshaken. Two streams of gentle water trickled down the knight's cheeks and with a strangled whimper, Julia let her spear fall to the ground.

"You... You will die," Julia whispered.

"Of course, you blathering child," the old woman grimaced. The tall grass stirred beneath a gentle breeze's phantom touch. "But not today, I don't think."

Aveline allowed a sigh of relief, then wiped the beads of sweat from her brow. Setting her pack down beside the prisoner, the girl set about stitching and dressing yet another tapestry of wounds. With a steady hand clad in decades of callous and scar, the prisoner gestured at the girl.

"Some squire you have here," Margot cringed as Aveline tightened a reddening, cotton bandage.

"Someday she'll be a knight, I have little doubt," Julia replied without emotion, her eyes trained on the brightening horizon. Mother and daughter sat in silence for a time as Aveline shifted her green eyes back and forth between the two and set about her work. Wispy orphan remnants of storm clouds drifted slow overhead. Out among the grassy fields, a pair of sparrows chattered as a hawk circled above.

"What name did you take?" Margot wondered. Her voice was low and earnest.

"The Shining Knight," Julia admitted. Blushing, the young woman pulled her tattered gold cloak close. A shadow of a grin passed over Margot's age-riven lips.

"One worthy of your plate, to be sure," the old woman chuckled.

"You'd rather I'd taken after you? Been called a 'beast' and spent my days blood-soaked and snarling?"

"Ah, 'Knight of Beasts.' I always liked the name. Felt true, honest," Margot confided. With each word, her voice grew more pensive. "There was a time when I believed as you do that the oaths and ideals made me better than most. A beautiful weapon forged over years to be a 'knight.' Revered by the people, beloved by king and country! But in time I came to see that we are all beasts...

There are no beautiful weapons. Warriors, soldiers, killers. Protect the innocent. Serve the crown. Defeat the enemy. No matter the words, knights are no better than dogs, bred to bay for the favor of the crown."

"Not even dogs abandon their young. Not even beasts."

Margot fixed a stare at her daughter for a long moment, then returned her gaze to the sun. Aveline remained silent, trying hard not to be seen between sutures.

"Those lofty ideals you seem to love make prisoners of us all, Shining Knight. The things I've done in the name of honor and chivalry... The blood shed... After your loyal father died at the hands of his master, I decided that the only knight deserving of the title is the beast who wants it least. Without me you had a chance to be something better," the old woman whispered. "I didn't want you to walk the same path of regret."

"And yet..." Julia said, brow furrowed in anger. The red-tailed hawk fell like an arrow from the sky, shrieking terror at its prey. It was a long time before the Shining Knight spoke again, but when she did, her voice was somber and resolved. "Aveline, give her your pack."

"What will you tell the king?" The prisoner asked. "You return without the beast, they'll think you one as well."

"I'll think of something," Julia replied, glancing at Aveline. The girl nodded. "Be on your way already, old woman, before someone sees you and we're all hanged for treason."

With knight and squire beneath each arm, the prisoner struggled to her feet, weathered face scrunched in quiet pain. Aveline raised her canvas sack, straps heavy with sword and shield. Threading her arms through its loops, the old woman hefted it onto her back, then winced at its weight. One by one she surveyed Aveline's bandages, nodding at the thorough work.

"You saved two lives today. Hannah would be proud," the woman concluded.

Aveline averted her eyes, then stepped away, blushing.

"Should you grow tired of the charade, I'll be waiting," the Knight of Beasts muttered. Turning to Julia, Margot held out a trembling hand to caress her daughter's cheek, but said nothing. The two women gazed at one another again, their brown eyes, black hair, and solemn faces like reflections across time. "But perhaps... Perhaps you will yet prove me wrong."

Without waiting for a reply, the old woman turned and started limping toward the trees. After a moment she had vanished beyond the oak, ash, and shade. Aveline raised a red hand to bid farewell.

"Nothing but ruin in her wake," Julia said flatly, watching her mother depart. The knight's pale lips lifted below somber eyes.

"I don't know," Aveline murmured. Faint memories of another woman—her bright green eyes and head of hazel hair couched in blue fabric—swam in the girl's mind. Melancholy warmth spread throughout her chest as Aveline touched the azure cloak wrapped around her body. "What will we tell the guards?"

"The prisoner fled in the night. Taken by shadow and beast," the knight supposed. Julia shook her head, then started hobbling through the field toward the city.

Aveline turned to follow, but a movement in the darkness caught her attention. Just beyond the forest's threshold, two forlorn, shining eyes watched Julia depart. Her own eyes glimmering, Aveline smiled before running to catch the knight.

A KNIGHT DEFENDS THOSE WEAKER

A KNIGHT IS TRUE AND FAITH

JUST AND SHREW

AND GRAND TO BEHOLD

A KNIGHT UPHOLDS HONOR

FOR THOSE WHO CANNOT

TLOT
TLOT
TLOT
TLOT-TLOT
TLOT-TLOT

DIN?!
DIN IS THAT YOU

...

SHIT.

I AM NOT A KNIGHT

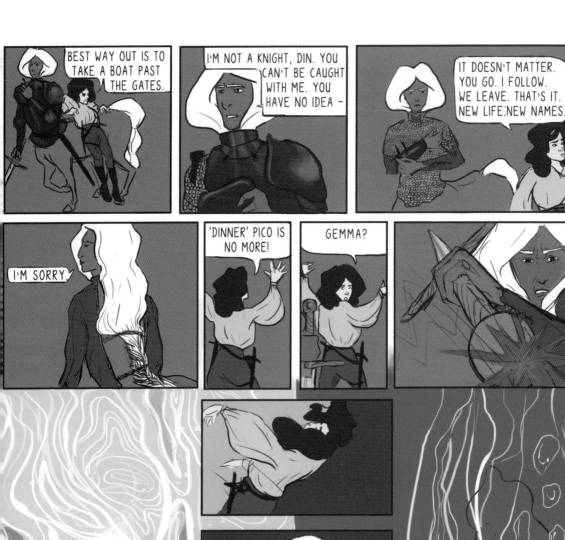

I AM NOT A KNIGHT.

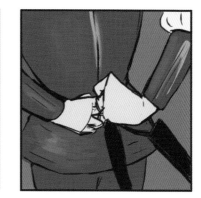

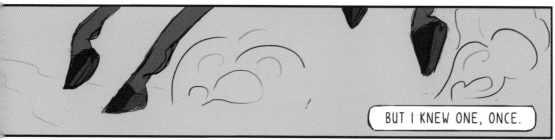

BUT I KNEW ONE, ONCE.

OF STEEL
BY NICOLE PURPORA

Black smoke fills the lungs of my memories
of battles and blood that tastes
copper in my mouth

copper like cheap blades and the shields of man
that I would never hold
if it weren't for breasts bound and short breaths
and hair falling on tiled floor

Unnecessary flesh is no use to me
it's dissonant with my soul
and at odds with the drum that keeps time in my ribs

You are the best man I have ever known

But I am not a man at all
forged of steel and of steel my blade shall be
for steel only knows resolve
and of that I have never been poor

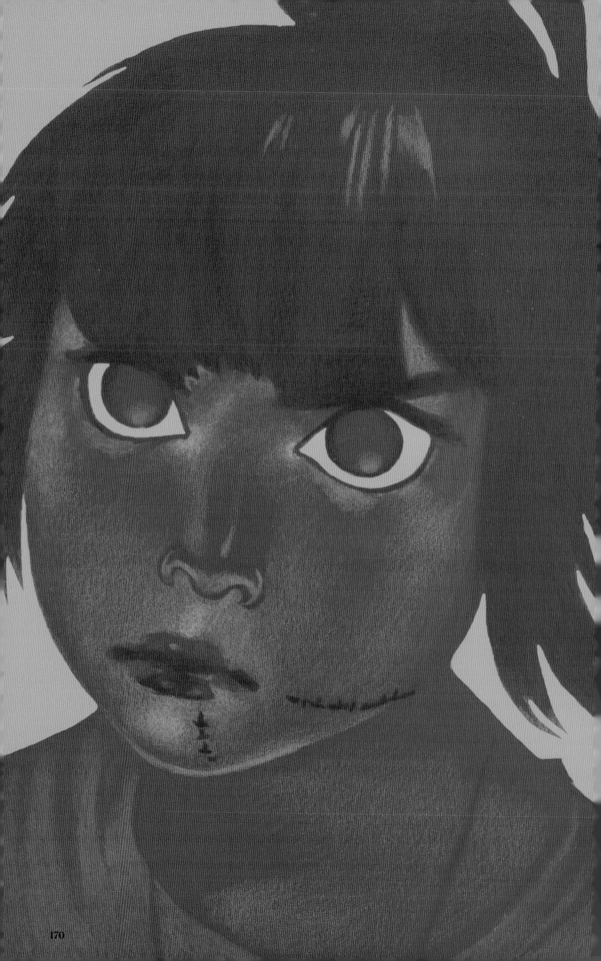

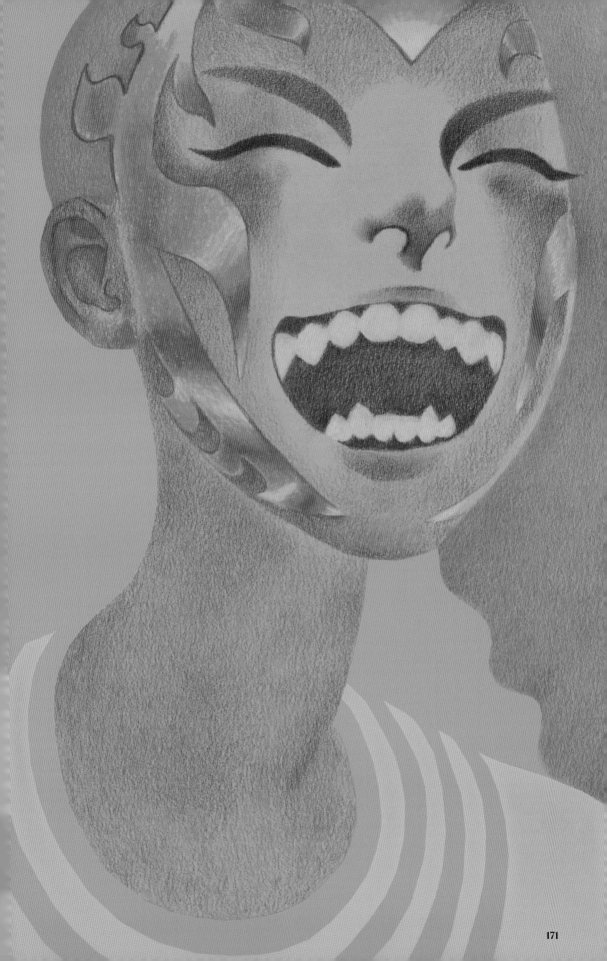

SELF – SAVIOR

Hazel Newlevant

In chivalric code, a knight's duty is to serve and protect a lady. These roles are deeply intertwined.

A lady knight saves herself. I seek to embody both principals.

Gentilness comes easily to me,
but I often let others carry my anger.

Now I charge myself with my own protection.

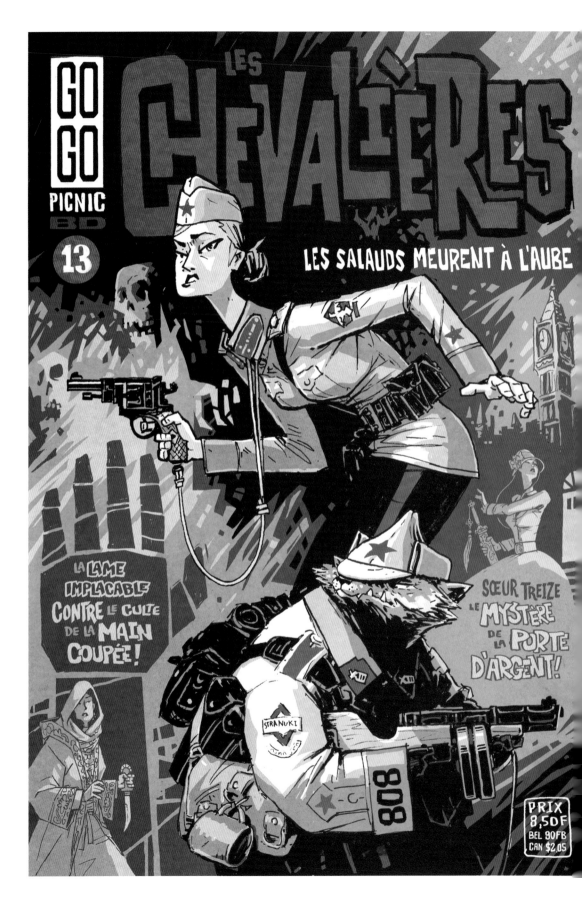

YOU MUST BE KIDDING ME

AND IN A GODDAMN CITY TOO

LET ME REPHRASE THAT

HUMANS ARE NOT AN APPROPRIATE PART OF DRAGON DIET AND AS A SPECIES DRAGONS DON'T KILL HUMANS FOR AMUSEMENT

YOUR ACTIONS ARE NOT CAUSED BY THE SPECIFIC OF YOUR SPECIES AND ALSO NOT BY ANY CONFLICT

BUT BY YOUR OWN TWISTED SADISTIC PERSONALITY AND DISREGARD FOR THE LAW

TSK!

YOU'RE AN EDUCATED PEST

AND I KNOW YOU'RE A WANTED CRIMINAL

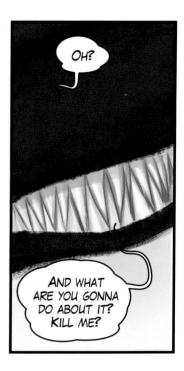

OH?

AND WHAT ARE YOU GONNA DO ABOUT IT? KILL ME?

BORED.

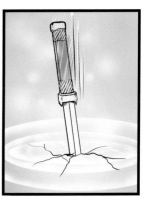

LEND ME YOUR SWORD OR I'LL TAKE IT MYSELF.

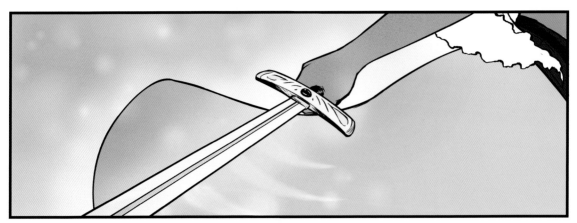

UH, IT DIDN'T HOLD UP AFTER ALL...

MY SWOOORD

AAAAW, IT'S ALREADY OVER?

IT LOOKS LIKE A DRAGON KNIGHT WAS AROUND

AREN'T DRAGON KNIGHTS SUPPOSED TO BE FRIENDS WITH DRAGONS, NOT DRAGON SLAYERS?

AREN'T THEY A LEGEND?

OH, THEY'RE LEGENDARY

ALYSSA~!

MAYLA! HAVEN'T SEEN YOU FOR AGES.

THERE'S BEEN NO WORD ABOUT YOU IN AGES

OR...

I KNEW IT!

YOU WERE THE ONE WHO STOPPED THE MONSTER IN THANOS!!

...YEAH...

REALLY?

AND YOU LET OTHERS TAKE THE CREDIT?

I'M TRYING TO KEEP A LOW PROFILE...

THIS IS CITY WATCH!

PLEASE PREPARE YOUR KNIGHT IDs AND WEAPONS PERMITS

UH, GREAT... I DON'T HAVE MINE ON ME, I'M ON HOLIDAY...

I'M PRETTY SURE THIS KNIGHT WILL GLADLY TAKE THE CREDIT FOR THE DRAGON

I CAN'T TAKE CREDIT FOR SOMETHING I HAVEN'T DONE!

WELL IT WAS YOUR SWORD...

I WOULD DO IT BUT PEOPLE SAW YOU AT THE SCENE

ALL RIGHT

BUT YOU'LL TAKE THE REWARD

I STILL OWE YOU A SWORD, THOUGH

POSEN·DAILY

25h March 17724

Dragon attacking the city stopped by a passing knight

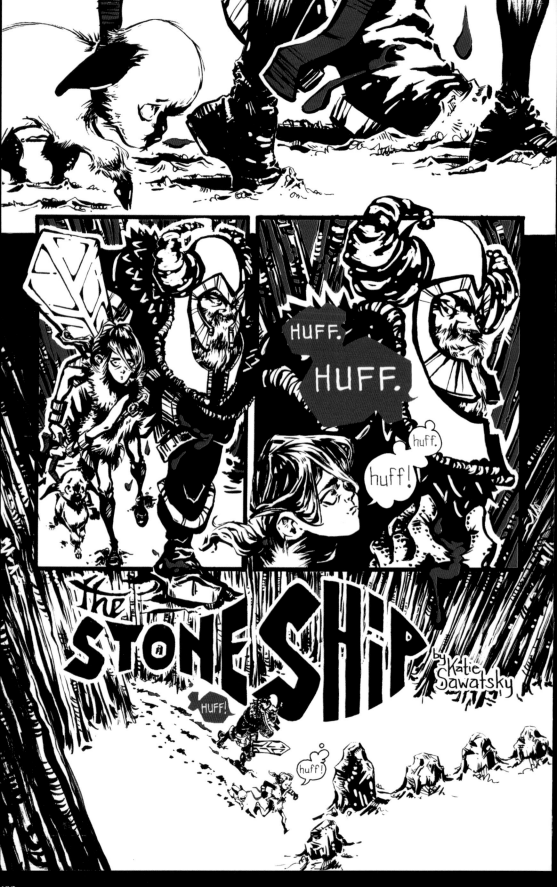

everyday knight

TAKE IT ON THE CHIN

IMMOLATION

CLEMENTE   LÓPEZ ORTIZ   SOUTAR

WHEN A STORM GATHERS

YOU BATTEN DOWN THE HATCHES

AND HOPE FOR CALM

BUT HOPE CAN ONLY GET YOU SO FAR.

FUMP

FORTUNE REWARDS SACRIFICE

AND I INTEND TO GIVE

CHK!

EVERYTHING.

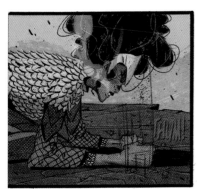

ONLY THEN CAN VICTORY BE

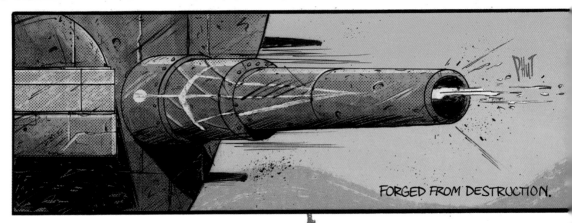

FORGED FROM DESTRUCTION.

AVMMMMBBB

IT IS SAID THAT
CONSTANT FLAME
IS AGONY

IF THAT IS TRUE...

I AM BEYOND
THE PAIN.

KRA-KOOM

FSSSH

THOUGH OUR MISSION IS COMPROMISED

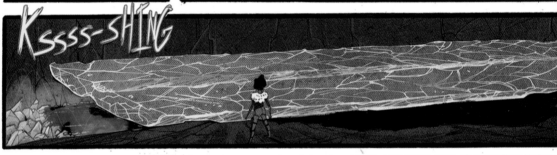

Kssss-SHING

MERCY IS NEVER AN OPTION.

BY HER ORDERS...

217

LISTEN TO MY PREY...

THEY CRY OUT IN FEAR.

IF MY AIM IS TRUE

FORTUNE WILL SMILE ON US ALL.

MY BONES RACK WITH ACHES

AND ALL I HEAR IS HOLLOW NOISE.

SUCH IS THE PRICE OF POWER.

MY SWORD...

KRAK

CL-CLAK

CL-CLAK

CL-CLAK

BY SHEER FORCE OF WILL

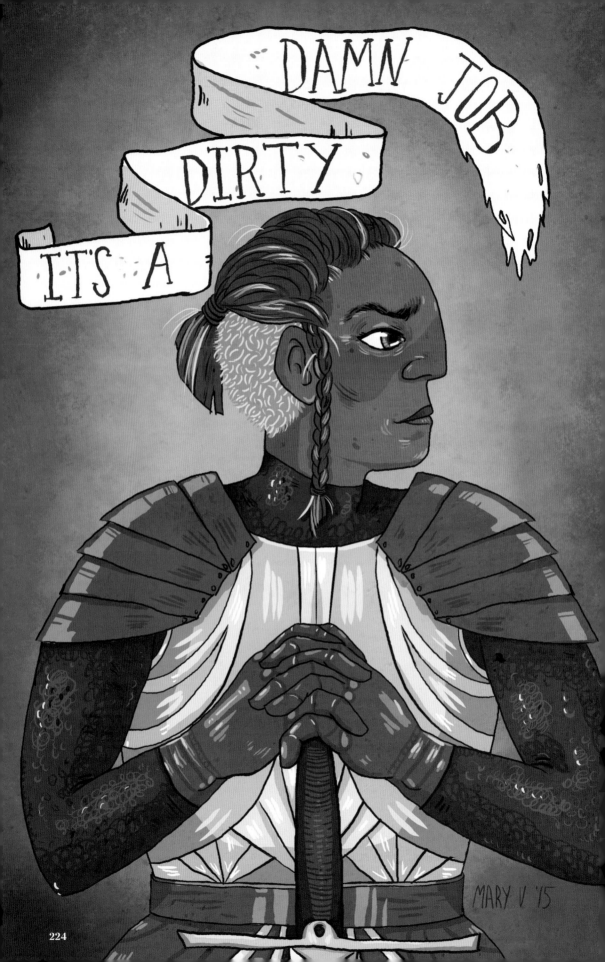

THE REPORTER
Jordan Witt

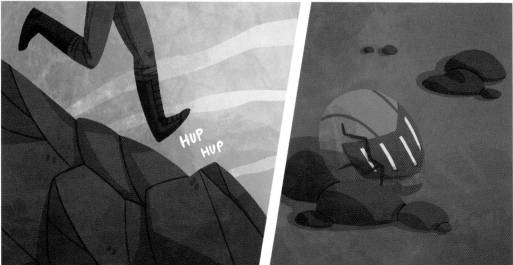

YOU'RE THAT REPORTER.

I SAW YOU ON THE NEWS.

YOU'RE PUTTING YOURSELF IN DANGER TO GET THOSE PICTURES.

I DIDN'T...

I DIDN'T TAKE A PICTURE OF YOU WITHOUT YOUR HELMET, IF YOU WERE WORRIED ABOUT THAT.

I WON'T TELL ANYONE WHAT YOU LOOK LIKE.

YOUR DISCRETION IS APPRECIATED.

AN ODE TO THE QUEEN WHO CHOSE DIGNITY OVER CROWN
BY CARIS CRUZ

It was midday, he was merry
in a drunken fit he called you,
to parade yourself amongst a throng of faces
people you don't even know.

When the order was, "Wear the crown,
or abandon it forever."
You chose the latter with firm decision.
There was no regret.

No king can ever tell you, "Come here,"
and show some swagger. You are his royal consort,
not a claim; a partner, not a property.
Diadems are not titles you sign with your head.

Vashti, it's your choice
to wear a blanket or a ball gown. Your body
is not a trophy. Your beauty
is not for entertainment of
intoxicated monkeys shaped like men.

Hear my applause, the only one
ringing as you walk out of the palace
wearing not a crown but a sack.
No tiara can lessen the brilliance of your charm.

Strut away with stronger legs, you lost your queenship
but still you have your dignity. It is
your most prized possession and no one
can ever take that away.

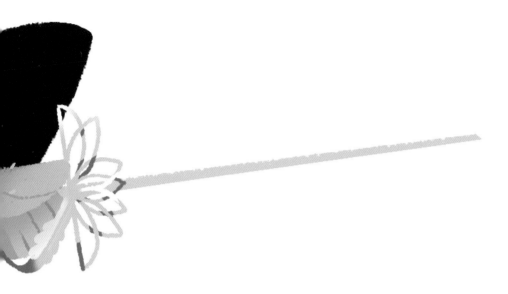

To the courageous & fantastic Kickstarter backers whose
generosity and support have made this book a reality,

All of your names will forever live in our hearts
and at onethousandandoneknights.com/thankyou

MEET THE KNIGHTS

The Knights of Courage were asked to define knighthood, how they each gather strength and find sources of inspiration.

A SPARROW Pg. 202-203
What is a knight? You're supposed to put a human in a metal wrapper and tell it to go poke things I think. Also something about royalty and dragons but mainly poking things. I think if you are the ruler of the land you can tell it not to poke you which is nice.

@madeofsparrows   ofsparrows.tumblr.com

ALUMINUMBUNNY Pg. 162
Being both feminine and strong is completely possible. Femininity and strength are more than simply outward appearances.

www.aluminumbunny.com   @aluminumbunny   aluminumbunny.tumblr.com

AYO, DARRYL Pg. 27-33
The strength of a character comes from the clarity of intention with which they were created as well as the complexity and nuance with which the character is explored within the narrative.

www.littlegardencomics.com   @darrylayo   darrylayo.tumblr.com

AZIM, FAHMIDA Pg. 237
To me strength of character comes down to being able to do what needs to be done. Strength is being afraid- it's recognizing your fear but not letting it take control. Someone who can stare their fear in the eyes and still move forward has the makings of an unconquerable soul.

www.fahmida-azim.com   @Eemajin   agent-eemz.tumblr.com

BAILEY, STEPHANIE Pg. 240
Strength is meeting adversity head on, even if you fall short, it's in the attempt and in the drive that fuels someone to persevere. In the darkest hour, strength is the smallest step forward.

@lonniebegood   Lonniebegood.tumblr.com

BARTEL, JEN Pg. 241
True strength comes from an unwavering desire to stay true to one's moral compass, even when it's difficult and goes against the beliefs of those who choose an easier road. When this desire is funneled into protecting those weaker than ourselves and finding the courage to stand up for what is right, we are unstoppable.

www.jenbartel.com   @heyjenbartel   jenbartel.tumblr.com

BLETSIS, GEORGE Pg. 34
To me strength isn't physical power, but a state of mind. It's the ability to carry on, regardless of what others will think or say, and no matter what obstacles are thrown at you. Carry on being yourself, carry on doing what you're passionate about, and carry on supporting those you love.

www.monstertree.co.uk   @geeblets   monstertreeart.tumblr.com

BURR, TANYA Pg. 50
Strength, to me, is not just how many pounds you can bench press. It's knowing the weight of the world, the weight of your own existence, and still being able to get up, go to work/school/both, and continue on each day, making the world brighter in any way you can. It's easy to give in to hopelessness, into routine, but it takes courage to follow your dreams, knowing what challenges your ambitions may bring.

www.tanyamburr.com   @tanyamburr   tanyamburr.tumblr.com

CHAUTIN, ALEX Pg. 37–39

Strength means giving a little bit more of yourself than you thought was possible when you began.

www.eeriepd.com @achaunyan teachercomic.tumblr.com

CHEESEMAN, EMILY Pg. 18–25

What makes a knight a knight is their sense of duty and devotion. They find their strength in the thing to which they've pledged their sword. My inspiration comes from a love of stories and a desire to share them—to inspire readers with a tale of virtues that last far beyond the fairytale.

www.emilycheeseman.com @emcheeseman emstantinople.tumblr.com

CHEN, YUNSHU Pg. 65

Someone who fights against dictatorship— all Chinese girls who struggle to be born, survive, and speak for their own rights.

www.haywillouis.com @chenyunshu haywillouis.tumblr.com

CHIU, ALEX Pg. 47–49

I wanted to write a story about two girls fighting big bad evil spirits together. How often do we get to see two females co-star in a story, let alone pull the punches (literally)? Girls stick together, not turn on each other when one of them attains success and the other didn't. Strength is courage for yourself and for your friend(s); strength is supporting each other, and strength is perseverance. Fight on, Ami and Emi, and all of the other ladies out there!

www.alexmchiu.com @alexmchiu chiumonster.tumblr.com

CHRISTENSON, HANNAH Pg. 35

Strength can mean so many different things depending on the situation. Brawn, stamina, soundness, passion, power, force, vehemence, skill, backbone. One thing that I find myself dwelling on is the kind of strength that inspires action, that invisible thing that pushes you to make a move, the feeling in the pit of your gut that propels you onward through your battles. It can be a merciful and quiet capability, or a thunderous spirit. Strength, to me, is showing true mettle in the face of adversity, and having the audacity to believe you can overcome.

www.hannahchristenson.com @hannah_illo hannahchristenson.tumblr.com

CHUNG, CHRISTINA Pg. 51

Strength to me means overcoming your fears and self-doubts, and being able to fully trust yourself. Strength is admitting to your own mistakes, and having the courage to amend them. Strength is putting the needs of others before your own.

www.christina-chung.com @christina.illustrates christinaillustrates.tumblr.com

CLEMENTE, ZACHARY Pg. 210–222

A Knight is an individual who occupies a role requiring the balanced application of love, sacrifice, and power in service of a cause other than their own, however that shakes out.

www.clemente.works @clementeworks

COHEN, RACHEL L. Pg. 53–61

What makes someone a knight is their drive to help those in need. Their armor not only comes in the form of metal plates, but in the drive to protect the ones they love.

www.rlcohenart.com @kat326 capskat26.tumblr.com

CRUZ, CARIS Pg. 64, 236

Wherever there is passion, wherever there is fire. You can find it in poetry, in numbers, in sciences;when you catch a bus en route to school or by watching the ocean tides rip through the shore. Even right now, there are hidden traces of bravery in the lines of your palms.

www.hellocaris.com @hellocaris mostunlikely.tumblr.com

DEGRAAF, LAUREN Pg. 17

For me what makes a character strong is when they are able to identify their fears and flaws and get past them to complete their goals.

@degraala degraala.tumblr.com

DEMINO, MATTHEW Pg. 45

Strength to me is the ability to face failure. There are a few inevitabilities in life, One of those is, at some point you will fail. Being strong is facing the fact that you will fail, and knowing that you will recover from it. Knowing that at some point you will not succeed, prepares you to overcome any fear of defeat. Once you accept that fact, you can turn any defeat into the tools to battle your failure. And with those tools you will overcome any loss. Failing does not make you a failure. You don't have to battle monstrosities to be a knight. You have to battle failure, and overcome it. Then you will be strong, and you will find great success in your losses.

www.mattdemino.artstation.com   mattdemino.deviantart.com   @mattdemin   mattdemino.tumblr.com

DENSFORD, IAN Pg. 70-71

The will & drive to do what is necessary. to follow through despite the odds or suggested fate. to have a heart that is compassionate, but also a mind that is courageous enough to listen to it. and most importantly, really good magical items, crafted by skilled hands.

www.iandensford.com   @iandensford   iandensford.tumblr.com

DUFFY, MELISSA Pg. 42-43

Strength in my eye: PRAGMATISM in the face of insurmountable pain — of which, in this life, is much.

www.melissatheduffy.com   @melissatheduffy   melissatheduffy.tumblr.com

DUNLAP, ROYAL Pg. 66-69

What makes a character strong can be defined three different ways: physically, mentally, and morally strong. They can posses the physical strength of a God or the supernatural. A strong-willed person can attain wisdom in how to use said strength, and whether they use that strength for the good of the world or for selfish purposes and goals. I like characters who can have unrealistic strengths but relatable and down-to-earth weaknesses, and that in turn can make a character well diverse and more approachable to their audience.

www.radimudio.com   @radimudio   radimudio.tumblr.com

ENDURO Pg. 63

Strength is the ability to be brave and act in support of your beliefs!

www.mightier.tumblr.com   @ochentiocho   mightier.tumblr.com

ESPINOSA, ANISSA Pg. 46

To me, a Knight is someone who acts in the service of and for the benefit of others. They go against the grain of what society expects of them, stand by their convictions, and follow their hearts in order to make a difference.

@redribbonrobot   redribbonrobot.tumblr.com

ESPIRITU, NARCISO Pg. 36, 52

The best kind of strength, motivation, inspiration comes from the people around you. They can do all kinds of different things in their lives, but as long as they love you and cheer you on in whatever you do, that kind of strength never fails. And tacos. The best strength comes from tacos.

www.narcisoespiritu.com   @narcisoespiritu   narcisoespiritu.tumblr.com

EVIN, DELIA Pg. 74-75, 77

A Knight is a fantasy, a reality, the inner strength of a person. A Knight is a combination of real and make-believe. A child's dream, an artist's vision. A Knight is a character, a being, that to me is the embodiment of honor, of everything that I love about fantasy and science-fiction books, and a piece of history come to life.

www.deliaevin.com   @deliaevin   deliaevinart.tumblr.com

FRANKLIN, LYNNETTE Pg. 79

Strength isn't just physical. Believing in yourself is a kind of strength, too!

www.littlewhiteoctopus.com   @littlewhiteocto

GARCIA, XAVIER Pg. 78

Any of us can become a knight. It is a matter of standing up not just yourself, but for the plights of others. It is not about swords, sorcery or fancy armor but rather about what you can do to become that person others can rely on. We can all be knights.

www.raging-spaniard.com   @ragingspaniard   ragingspaniard.tumblr.com/

GINDLESPERGER, RYAN Pg. 80-81

Everyone is strong in their own way. We have to be. What sets a knight apart is how they use that strength. They stand as a pillar not just for themselves, but for anyone else they possibly can. That's the key; wiling and capable service.

www.masterycomic.com   @masterycomic   masterycomic.tumblr.com

GOMEZ, CHARLOTTE Pg. 82-83

Strength is a willingness to question the things you hold closest. Being true to yourself is important, but change is no less vital. (And usually much harder.)

www.charlottegomez.com   @ccharlottegomez   charlottegomez.tumblr.com

HANSON , CHRISTOPHER Pg. 108-109, 238-239

To me, the mark of true strength, is the unabashed willingness to be yourself.

www.christopherlhanson.com   chris-hanson.deviantart.com

HARVEY, GLENN Pg. 41

A knight to me, is anyone who has a firm set of ideals that sets the tone for how they live their life - a code if you will. Being a knight isn't easy. It takes a lot of guts to stick to what you believe in, and that's always been true regardless of any time or setting.

www.glenn-harvey.com   @drawglenndraw   glharvey.tumblr.com

HIRAISHI, MICHELLE Pg. 40

To me a strong character is one that overcomes an internal struggle and becomes a capable and independent individual. They develop into a force to be reckoned with and feel more secure with their identity.

michellehiraishi.tumblr.com

HODDY, MATTHEW K. Pg. 85-90

Conviction enough to see the toughest things through to the end

www.spacepyrates.com   @mkhoddy   mkhoddy.tumblr.com

HOWARD, TAIT Pg. 84

Strength is about being able to lift really heavy stuff, like crazy huge boulders or a giant cursed sword or the emotional burdens of your loved ones.

www.comicbooktakeover.com   @taitcomics

HUNT, MEG Pg. 92-93

Strength is not just physical (although that helps); it's a mix of curiosity, resilience, and tenacity that allows you to keep moving forward and exploring the world with wonder and respect.

www.meghunt.com   @meghunt

HUYNH, OLIVIA Pg. 94-95

Strength: To me, strength is the part of you that keeps growing, even when you're uprooted, over-watered, neglected, or in too bright or dark a place for comfort

www.oliviawhen.com   @usuallyawake   oliviawhen.tumblr.com

JAROCKI, MAREK Pg. 96-107

We can all find strength within ourselves. You may not feel it but its there. It may not be easy to find, but once you do seize it and use it. You can do anything.

www.youtube.com/marekjarocki   @mjarocki_art   marekjarocki.tumblr.com

KAN, CRYSTAL Pg. 110-111

To me, strength is the ability to learn. Learning to overcome your own flaws and weaknesses. Learning to accept others for who they are, despite your differences. Learning to expand your own horizons and picking up new skills. Everyday, we strive to improve ourselves through education, which gives us the strength to move forward, together.

www.crystalkan.com @wizardofkitty wizardofkitty.tumblr.com

KANE, KATA Pg. 113-120

Strength is devotion, and always believing in yourself!

www.kata-kane.com www.altar-girl.com @kata_kane altar-girl.tumblr.com

KAO, STEPHANIE Pg. 123

There is always more to someone then what we see. They have hidden aspects, invisible armor, that gives them strength beyond what our sight tells us.

www.zetallis.com @eldritchsky zetallis.tumblr.com

KOLB, ANDREW Pg. 124-125

I think strength comes from the ability to decide. Whether it's fight or flight, the decision will always be better than inaction. You'll critical miss 100% of the dice you don't roll.

www.kolbisneat.com @kolbisneat

LASTER, RHONDA Pg. 126-127

I think what makes someone strong is their willingness to help others. A knight defends those who need help.

www.rllcreative.com @rhonda_lauren

LAUGHINGBEAR Pg. 206

Strength is not always loud and bold— strength can be gentle, subtle, the courage to take breaks and try again another day. Fighting monsters, protecting a village, and even growing up are all battles that need to be fought sometimes. Everyone is a knight in some way... so fight on, fellow knights!

www.laughingbear.us @gelatobear laughingbear.tumblr.com

LEDGERWOOD, MARK Pg. 62

We are a culmination of the good and bad deeds done to and for us. Be the good.

www.mledgerwood.com @markledgerwood instagram.com/markledgerwood

LEE, ANDY Pg. 121

I could answer this with an entire essay but ultimately, I think a strong person is someone with a big heart. (Metaphorically, but physically works too!)

@andythelemon andythelemon.tumblr.com

LEFAVE, KALLIE Pg. 163, 207

I find inspiration and strength through seeing and perceiving the world around me. Striving to understand and embrace the world allows creativity to spark and resilience to grow, with the hope that I can bring others inspiration and strength as well.

www.kallielef.deviantart.com @kallielef kallielef.tumblr.com

LOISH Pg. 10

To me, being a knight meants to show strength. Strength means balance. It means harmony with your surroundings, sensitivity to the world around you, and the ability to form alliances and bonds that will make not only you, but also others around you strong

www.loish.net @loishh

LUO, AMEORRY Pg. 129

I've always thought of Knights as characters who are leaders and steadfast in their cause or trade. To me, a strong or inspiring character has always meant one with intrigue; secrets and the idea of dormant power are some of my favorite themes. I'm especially drawn to multi-faceted characters that seem like they have hidden stories or reasons behind their actions, regardless of whether they're physically strong or ethically sound.

www.dustandhalos.com   dustandhalosart.tumblr.com   @dustandhalos

MACHICADO, SHEILA Pg. 132

I believe strength is having the courage to protect what is most important to you, even if you feel like you don't have the power to do so. You would do anything to make sure that whom or what you're protecting is safe and out of harms way.

www.smachicado.com   @glazedbagel

MAYNARD, ALYSSA Pg. 156–161

A knight is sometimes meek, and undeserving, and perhaps still looking for the strength within themselves to rise.

www.alyssamaynard.com   @alyssamaynard   alyssasketches.tumblr.com

MCGINLEY, CLAIRE Pg. 122

Strength is the ability to keep going through things that are hard, whether physical or mental. It's being able to push past the things that limit you so you can continue to develop.

www.claires.ink   @claires_ink

MCGOVERN, ALEC Pg. 72–73

What does strength mean to me? Why It's the most important ability score for a barbarian or fighter!

stuffyreyeswithwonder.tumblr.com

MCKERNAN, DEVIN Pg. 138–151

A "knight" is not defined by martial prowess or the words of an oath. A true knight need only struggle daily and honorably to be the best human he or she can be.

www.aknightadrift.com   @aknightadrift   whatslenderthreads.com

MCMORRIS, KELLEY Pg. 11, 44, 152–153, 173

A knight is someone who lays down their life in order to protect the weak and helpless.

www.kmcmorris.com   @kelleymcmorris

MEEKS, MIRANDA Pg. 166

Strength means to endure, even when there's a strong desire to give up. It means boldness in the face of uncertainty, even if part of you wants to surrender. In short, true strength is forcing confidence to overcome feelings of frailty and self-doubt, even when it's difficult to do so.

www.mirandameeks.com   @miranda_meeks   miranda-meeks.tumblr.com

MEYER, THOMKE Pg. 16, 131

Honesty.

thomkemeyer.tumblr.com

MODESTI, MELANIE Pg. 76, 154–155, 209

A Knight is more than a suit of armor and does more than slay dragons. They can be anyone who embodies the values of the people like hope, strength, leadership, courage, and inspiration. I wanted to portray girls with unique abilities who are representing all of these things.

@christinaSketch   christinasketch.tumblr.com

MYLER, JAKE Pg. 136-137

Real strength is the ability to support your friends, helping them to be as courageous and powerful as they can be!

www.jakemyler.com   @lazesummerstone   jakemyler.tumblr.com

NEWLEVANT, HAZEL Pg. 174-175

To me, strength means perseverance, and standing up for the vulnerable. Sometimes that vulnerable person is yourself.

www.newlevant.com   @hnewlevant   newlevant.tumblr.com

OFTEN, MELODY Pg. 170-171

A knight, or archetypal warrior, honors life and death with a purity that transcends obedience bringing closure to the wavering and defense to the abused. For some warriors the greatest foe can be that which is created internally, both universal and omniscient.

www.melodyoftenillustrates.tumblr.com   @melodyoften   trinadot.tumblr.com

ORTIZ, RICARDO LOPEZ Pg. 210-222

To me one's strength is measured by our determination. Determination is the key to tearing down all the walls that block your path to success. You can have all the talent or inspiration in the world, but if you don't have the determination to see things through. You'll achieve nothing.

www.rlopezortiz.com   @rlopezortiz

OTT, COLE Pg. 176-177

Strength comes from struggle.

www.coleottart.com   @coleott   coleott.tumblr.com

PAE, SHANEN Pg. 178

To face the world in all its multitude, to bear one's heart to fear, grief, and love, and to emerge not a victim, but a Knight.

shanenpae.tumblr.com

PAIK, EMILY Pg. 179

Strength means the courage to fight. It's easy to think that strength means beating everyone else or winning all your battles. However, for me, strength means not giving up or losing faith in the face of any nagging insecurities, seemingly insurmountable obstacles, or paralyzing fears. I find strength in the people who have the courage to fight the hard battles and make the hard choices knowing full well that they could lose.

emilypaik.tumblr.com

PEREZ MARQUEZ, BARBARA Pg. 12, 128

Resilience is the measuring system of strength, standing up one more time to any challenge. Being brave, a little or a lot, for something big or small lets our strength shine through to the world.

www.mustachebabs.com   @mustachebabs

PHILLIPS, RORY Pg. 180

A Knights strength comes from self-reliance. Independent and rational in thought and action. True to their ideals and staunchly defending them against any assault.

www.gogopicnic.com   @gogo_picnic   gogopicnic.tumblr.com

PIECHOWIAK, J. Pg. 181-190

When I think of knights I think of honor and courage. I don't think honor means the same thing to everyone; for me it's holding on to your own principles, which I think is much more important than following a set of arbitrary rules.

www.theothertentacle.com   @p_the_wanderer   p-the-wanderer.tumblr.com

PMURPHY   Pg. 168
Strong character means venturing into the unknown with wisdom and courage.

www.pmurphy.org

PODA, ATHINA K.   Pg. 130
Strength for me is found in standing up for what you believe in. Having support is important but even when you are on your own, being true to yourself and your beliefs is very empowering.

www.facebook.com/athinakpodaart

PURPORA, NICOLE   Pg. 169
Strength is the power to overcome, to live, and to keep going. To say you want to do something and accomplishing it no matter the struggles you face. The ability to be yourself 100% and do what makes you happy uncaring of what people think of you. I think strength is a much more internal power and one that can affect and inspire so many people around you. Your life is your own and to have the power to live it the way you want to and make it through any hardships is true strength to me.

@ichigoMakii   constellation-of-stars.tumblr.com   instagram.com/ichigo_maki/

RASMUSSEN-SILVERSTEIN, RHIANNON   Pg. 172
Strength and inspiration can be found in the world around you; just the act of seeing tomorrow, when the night is thickest, can be an act of defiance. If you don't keep fighting through the darkness, you might not get to see the next sunrise, and the sunrise is worth fighting for.

www.rhiannonrs.com   @charibdys   rhiannonrs.tumblr.com

R-GIE   Pg. 112
My definition of strength is when someone can go outside of their comfort zone and can surpass problems that were thrown at them. It can also mean waking up each morning, knowing the demons you'll be facing that day, but still managed to convince yourself to keep pushing forward.

www.r-gie.com   r-gie.tumblr.com

SANDERS, JACOB   Pg. 167
Strength is usually misconceived. When you think of someone who distinguishes themselves as strong, it can be disappointing for everyone involved. I suppose honor is something I value more. It warms my heart when one can act on a common, humanistic respect rather than playing the hero in their own narrow-sighted romantic story. Strength is, after all, the vehicle of that honor steers.

www.jacobsandersart.com   @jacobsandersart   jacobsandersillustration.tumblr.com

SAWATSKY, KATIE   Pg. 192-197
Knights are courageous. Knights are strong. And yet knights will fall. You can't count on knights. True heroics reside with those that take up that mythic mantle, and lead themselves through the dark forests.

@katiesawatsky   thisismyfacerightnow.tumblr.com

SCHANK, AMANDA   Pg. 13
When they work hard at something, even if they think they might be in over their head, and willingly face new challenges in order to better themselves.

www.amsbt.artstation.com

SEARLE, SARAH WINIFRED   Pg. 198-199
Strength is a necessary quality for kicking the butt of the tough-to-crack pickle jar that is life.

www.swinsea.com   @swinsea   swinsea.tumblr.com

SIEMENS, KAYSHA   Pg. 227
Sometimes knights come in unexpected forms...sometimes, they are the unnamed girl at the core of the familiar tale I chose to illustrate, a tale known only by the name of the impossible place she must reach to rescue her own husband: East of the Sun and West of the Moon. From her bravery and agency in freely choosing to marry a seeming beast for the sake of her family, to her courage across untold miles and impossible challenges to reclaim the one she loves, she transcends the moral trappings of her role in a parable that has been retold ever since Eros and Psyche. She chooses. She loves. She learns. She triumphs. To me, she is aknight.

www.kayshasiemens.com   kayshasiemens.tumblr.com

SOUTAR, ARIELLE Pg. 210-222
"One must use the night." —Tove Jansson
@howlingArielle   superarkfuntimes.tumblr.com

SOUTAR, TATIANA Pg. 201
Strength is in accepting that parts of you that are weak.
www.nearbyworlds.net   @birdstareart

SPARKS, BETH Pg. 200
To me, real strength is allowing yourself to be vulnerable...so then a knight is someone who is willing to be gentle and honest, who will strive to provide shelter to those who need it, and who will use their truth to try to make the world a better place.
www.solid-state-studios.com   @sparksel   sparkselart.tumblr.com

STINCHCOMBE, NIKKIE Pg. 164-165
Strength to me comes from those who are underestimated. I love characters who appear a certain way but shatter all stereotypes and assumptions. They're strong and fierce — both physically and psychologically and completely surpass the reader/viewers expectations.
www.littlepaperforest.com   @paperforest_   littlepaperforest.tumblr.com

STREJLAU, ALLISON Pg. 91, 226
Strength is being able to rely on others and put your faith in them fearlessly. Being able to do that means you and those close to you have proven themselves worthy and earned it.
www.allisonstrejlau.com   @astrejlau   astrejlau.tumblr.com

SYED, ANOOSHA Pg. 204-205
I'm Anoosha Syed, Potions Master and Knight extraordinaire! A knight is like a warrior of JUSTICE, who does everything in their power to do the right thing and protect others. They can come in all shapes and sizes (even in the 'short nerd' variety like me)!
www.anooshasyed.com   @foxville_art   foxville.tumblr.com

TER HORST, NIC Pg. 191
Strength is recognizing when you've come to the edge of your limits and need to ask for help, and acting when you can be that help for someone else.
www.nicterhorst.com   @nicterhorst   nicterhorstsketch.tumblr.com

THE THIRD RLM Pg. 133-135
A knight is neither good nor evil, man or woman, or limited by any single characteristic beyond their own drive. What defines a "knight" is the willingness and courage to fight for their beliefs, regardless the costs. A true knight fights for only for their truth
www.thethirdrlm.com   @thethirdrlm   thethirdrlm.tumblr.com

THOMASSON, PATRICIA Pg. 208, 223
I think a character can be considered strong when they bear the responsibility of what outcomes their actions produce—good or bad—and draw from an internal reserve to protect their loved ones and themselves.
www.pthomillu.com   @pthomillu   anticipatricia.tumblr.com

VERHOEVEN, MARY Pg. 224-225
I guess strength can be a lot of different things. Your ability to overcome obstacles, to help other people. Knowing yourself and knowing how to take care of yourself is also strength! Speaking up when it would be easier to keep quiet and being honest is incredibly strong. Also being able to open difficult jars. Strength can be many things, but as long as you use your strength to make things a bit better, I think that's the most important.
www.illustratingmary.com   @sob_comix

WITT, JORDAN Pg. 228-231

Strength means sticking to your convictions, standing up for people you love, and protecting those who can't protect themselves. A magic sword wouldn't hurt though.

www.52nddoor.com @jordannwitt 52nddoor.tumblr.com

WOO, JUSTIN Pg. 14-15

Strength means summoning the courage to face and overcome any obstacle, be it from an exterior or interior force, and always acting in accordance with the greater good.

www.justinwoo.net justinwwoo.tumblr.com

YOUNG, AIMEE Pg. 26, 232-235

Strength is having the will to keep on going no matter what the adversity is. Always being able to pull yourself up in any situation and being able to face things that you know will be challenging. I think that strength comes in many forms whether it be physical, emotional, or a combination of the two. Having a strong soul is what makes a person stand out, and be able to accomplish whatever they set their minds to, no matter who or what is in their way. That is what strength is to me.

www.bubble-rhapsody.deviantart.com @bubblerhapsodys bubblerhapsody.tumblr.com

Dear Reader,

Thank you for picking up this book. There are 1001 characters over the course of three volumes that make up 1001 Knights. The book in your hands is the first — **COURAGE**. Every artist and Kickstarter backer are knights and now by finishing this book, you are a part of this dialogue too.

Art can change us and inspire us to do great things. Now that you have read these stories, you can go forth and make the world a better place. Share this book, support and check out the 1001 Knights artists. You are always welcome in the 1001 Knights community.

RISE A KNIGHT.